Encyclopedia
of Bible Creatures

ENCYCLOPEDIA
OF
BIBLE CREATURES

by V. Møller-Christensen and K. E. Jordt Jørgensen

M. Theodore Heinecken, Editor

Arne Unhjem, Translator

Carol Wilde, Illustrator

FORTRESS PRESS • PHILADELPHIA

Translated from the original Danish version, *Bibelens Dyreliv,* published by De Unges Forlag, Copenhagen.

Library of Congress Catalog Card Number 65-21082

Printed in USA

3608G65   UB10

Editor's Preface
To the American Edition

In preparing Messrs. Möller-Christensen and Jörgensen's book
for the American reader, I was obliged to make certain changes
in the translation of the Danish text. The most important
of these involved quotations from the Bible. The reader
will note that almost all of the biblical passages in this edition are from the Revised Standard Version. Generally, in so
far as the identification of animals is concerned, this version
seems to be the most adequate. It does not, however, always
agree with the identification in the Danish Bible, which is
based on Luther's German translation. Nor does it, for that
matter, always agree with the consensus of present-day biblical
scholarship. In order to explain these matters wherever necessary, certain material had to be added that was not present
in the Danish text.

In adding the material at the bottom of the first page of
each entry, I was guided by the belief that handy reference
sections were a requirement in a book such as this, one of
the first popular books to attempt to cover the entire subject
of animal life in the Bible. This serves, I feel, two purposes:
it keeps much technical zoological information out of the
text, where it might unnecessarily mar the reader's enjoyment, and it saves the reader who is using the book as a reference tool the trouble of searching the text for the information
he desires.

Each of these extended "footnotes" includes information
about the zoological classification of the creature being taken
up. As a layman in this field, I was surprised to learn that

this classifying is not the cut-and-dried matter I had always supposed it to be, and that different sources offered varying classifications. I have attempted to be guided by the latest information currently accepted in this country, without going into too deep research. As the authors state in their preface, this book is not intended to be a zoology textbook, but rather an aid to the reader who wishes more enrichment and enjoyment in his reading of the Bible. The classifications here offered are intended simply to provide a general picture of the place of each creature in the animal kingdom. Both scientific names and common names are provided wherever it was possible to determine them.

The other item in the "footnote" comes under the heading "Lexicon." The listings here are transliterations, following Robert Young's *Analytical Concordance to the Bible,* of the Hebrew and Greek words that are used in the Bible to denote particular animals. Their inclusion here is not intended to be scholarly in any way, but rather to give the reader a "feel" for the way the biblical writers expressed themselves. In some cases, the careful reader will note how the characteristic sound made by an animal has helped shape the word; in others— particularly with the Greek—he will recognize cognates and original roots for English words.

Actually, the Danish edition provides Latin and Greek equivalents for the names of all the creatures listed, and the text often elaborates on these as well as on zoological questions, so the reference tools mentioned above merely expand and rearrange material set forth by the authors. There are changes in the text, however, that are not related to the "footnotes" and are not necessitated by the problem of the differences in the Danish and English Bibles noted in the first paragraph. Some verbal illustrations used by the authors would be perfectly familiar to the European reader, but are lost on an American; these have been paraphrased to convey the authors' meaning. In a relatively few instances, certain statements of the authors were not in accord with the generally accepted views of biblical scholars; more often than not, these are allowed to stand, since the authors have the right to express their own opinions. Occasionally, however, they do not fall into the category of opinion, and have been changed in accord with the facts. The guide for all such questions was the remarkably complete and reliable *Interpreter's Dictionary of the Bible,* published by Abingdon Press under the general editorship of Dr. George Arthur Buttrick.

The illustrations that appear in these pages have been chosen for the American edition and did not appear in the Danish edition. The majority of them are photographs of paintings and sculpture from the ancient Near East, particularly from Egypt and Assyria. The reader will thus get some idea of how the contemporaries of the biblical writers were struck by various animals, and how they expressed their reactions in art. Other illustrations are taken from the Christian era up to about A.D. 1500, and these reveal the way in which earlier Christians visually interpreted stories of the Bible in which animals play a part. Supplementary illustrations have been provided by realistic sketches of certain animals that are unfamiliar to most readers, as well as by photographs from life.

Finally, an appendix has been provided which lists, with brief comment, all of the names of animals that have been omitted from the main body of the text but which appear, whether justifiably or not, in either of our most popular Bible versions. Also included here are the mythological animals that occasionally make their appearance in the Bible. This book therefore is truly about *all* animal life in the Bible, that is, any form of animal life that might possibly have been mentioned in its pages.

The authors have made clear in their preface why they believe that such a book as this one should be written. Nothing more need be expressed, except the hope that the manner

in which this edition is presented will be of value to the
person who is seriously interested in understanding and ap-
preciating the Bible, a category which may include teachers,
ministers, students, and even that will-o'-the-wisp, the person
who enjoys a good book.

M. T. H.

Chicago, 1964

Authors' Preface

A person may go through the world with his eyes closed, blind to the beauty of mountains, woodlands, and seas, unaware of the teeming animal life of this earth, but no one can read the Bible without noticing the authors' fine and original gift for observing nature and their deep sense of awe for God's creative work. "Up, everything that God has made, to sing his praise and glory! The smallest of his works is great, and tells the wondrous story." The words of this Danish hymn are entirely in harmony with the descriptions of nature in the Bible.

It is self-evident that one should not expect instruction in natural science from the Bible. The Bible is not a textbook in zoology or botany; it is a proclamation of God's revelation in which he makes known his will to save. But this revelation wears the garb of time and place. It has been mediated through God's prophets and through the Son of God who became man, people who lived in Palestine two to three thousand years ago. When they proclaimed the word of God they used the colorful picture-language of the Orient. If we are to grasp the secrets of the kingdom of God we must learn to understand the same language. The reader of the present work should not expect to find here a handbook of zoology, but an aid in reading his Bible.

The writing of this book about animal life in the Bible has given the authors much joy and it has helped them to gain a deeper understanding of the Bible. If the same joy and help can be conveyed to the reader, the purpose of the work will have been achieved.

We cannot send this book out without expressing our warm appreciation to three men who have given valuable assistance in its preparation: Professors O. E. Ravn, Ph.D., and C. E. Sander-Hansen, Ph.D., who have furnished much valuable information, and Mr. H. Hastrup, M.A., who has kindly read the manuscript.

V. MØLLER-CHRISTENSEN
K. E. JORDT JØRGENSEN

Roskilde, 1952

Contents

MAMMALS

MOLLUSKS, FISH, REPTILES, AND WORMS

Illustrations

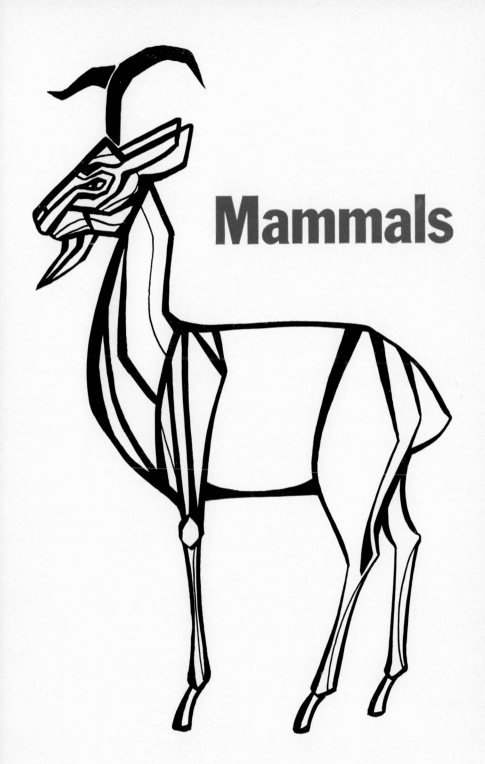

Mammals

The Antelopes

Of the several members of the antelope family to be found in ancient Israel, the most frequently mentioned in the Bible is the gazelle. Distantly related to the deer, it is noted for its beautiful and graceful body, its dark, friendly eyes, its lithe movements, and its great speed. A herbivorous (plant-eating) animal, the gazelle loves the open plains, where it lives in herds numbering up to fifty that roam from place to place in search of food. Gazelles are very shy, and they post guards to warn the herd of approaching danger, at the least sign of which they take flight. In swiftness the gazelle surpasses even the deer; in fact, few animals of any kind can compete with it. Even when it is fleeing, the gazelle seems to be aware of its superiority, for it leaps, almost arrogantly, three feet in the air as it runs.

The phrase "swift of foot as a gazelle" is used in the Old Testament to express the greatest degree of admiration for the agility and speed of either man or horse. For example,

---

CLASSIFICATION. (The name "antelope" is applied to several subfamilies of the Bovidae family, which includes oxen, sheep, goats, and others.) *Gazella dorcas* (the Dorcas gazelle), member of subfamily Antilopinae; *Addax nasomaculatus* (the addax) and *Oryx leucoryx* (the Arabian oryx), members of subfamily Hippotraginae; all in Pecora group (true ruminants) of order Artiodactyla (even-toed hoofed mammals).

LEXICON. Dorcas gazelle—*Hebrew:* TSEBI. Also, OPHER TSEBIYYAH (young gazelles). *Greek:* DORKAS. Addax—*Hebrew:* DISHON. Oryx—*Hebrew:* TEO, TO.

3

the chronicler of Israel's history during the reign of King
David describes Asahel the son of Zeruiah in this fashion.
However, Asahel's gazelle-like speed cost him his life, for it
enabled him to overtake the fleeing Abner, general of the late
King Saul's armies, who turned and pierced him with his spear
(II Sam. 2:18-23). The prophet Isaiah uses the picture of a
frightened gazelle when, in his prophecy about the fall of
Babylon, he wants to describe the fear and confusion of those
who are fleeing from the wrath of the Lord: "Like a hunted
gazelle . . . every man will turn to his own people" (Isa. 13:14).
Poetic uses of the image of the gazelle in flight may also be
found in Proverbs (6:5) and the Song of Solomon (8:14).

DORCAS GAZELLE

It is difficult to tell exactly what species of antelopes are
referred to in the Bible, but there are several that were prob-

Depicted above are two species of antelopes that may be
referred to in the Israelites' dietary laws. The addax (left)
is distinguished by its spiraling horns and goatlike mane, the
oryx by its extremely long horns. Both animals are still to be
found in biblical lands. (Drawing by Carol Wilde.)

ably familiar to biblical authors. The Dorcas gazelle is slightly smaller than a roe deer and much slimmer; its legs are incredibly thin. It has long, pointed ears and black, ringed horns bending backward and extending about eight inches. Its eyes are large and dark, its back is sand-colored and its

The graceful beauty of the gazelle is captured here in a sculpture by an unknown Egyptian artist of the fourteenth century B.C. (shortly before the Exodus). Unfortunately, the horns have been broken off. Note the extremely thin legs and the decorations on the base that represent desert plants. (Photograph courtesy of the Metropolitan Museum of Art. Figure from the Carnarvon Collection; gift of Edward S. Harkness, 1926.)

5

belly white. This species presently is found from Morocco and Algiers to the Red Sea and Syria. Perhaps the author of the Song of Solomon has this graceful animal in mind when he cries: "I adjure you, O daughters of Jerusalem, by the gazelles . . . of the field, that you stir not up nor awaken love" (Song of Sol. 2:7; 3:5). The bridegroom in the Song may be referring to the Dorcas gazelle when he compares the breasts of his beloved to "twins of a gazelle that feed among the lilies" (Song of Sol. 4:5; 7:3). It is possible that the Hebrew word *tsebi* (meaning "splendor") denoted this animal. In keeping with the gazelle's beauty, *tsebi* is also a root for women's names in Hebrew—for example, Zibiah, the mother of King Jehoash (II Kings 12:1).

THE ADDAX AND THE ORYX

The dietary laws of the ancient Israelites list several varieties of antelope, all of them among those animals that may be eaten. Besides the gazelle, there are two animals called by a variety of names in the different versions of the English Bible. One of these may well be the addax or Mendes antelope, while the other could be the Arabian oryx.

The two animals are closely related, but the addax differs from the oryx by dint of its spiraling horns. About the same size as a donkey, it is an off-white color, except for the head, which is brown; its body is closely covered with short hair, and it has a short mane on the underside of its neck which makes its head look like that of a goat. The hoofs are broad and flat, and the tail resembles a donkey's. The addax is common in Africa and Arabia, where it is hunted by the Arabs with falcons and dogs—a falcon is needed because no dog can overtake the fast, shy creature.

The oryx is white and has long, bent, sabre-like horns. Of all the antelopes mentioned in the Bible, it was probably the most frequently used for food; because of its long horns it was relatively easy to catch.

6

The Ape

The ape is mentioned in the Bible only once, in connection with the court of King Solomon. David's son lived in great luxury and oriental splendor in the royal palace at Jerusalem. His ships sailed the Red Sea to Ophir in Arabia—and possibly all the way to India and along the African coast as far south as Madagascar—to fetch the luxurious things required at a royal court. "For the king had a fleet of ships of Tarshish at sea with the fleet of Hiram. Once every three years the fleet of ships of Tarshish used to come bringing gold, silver, ivory, apes, and peacocks" (I Kings 10:22). We can only guess that the apes King Solomon procured were long-tailed monkeys of the guenon family which originally came from either Ethiopia or India.

In the ancient cultures of Egypt, Assyria, and India a good

CLASSIFICATION. ("Ape" can mean any type of monkey, but narrowly used refers to only those without tails.) *Cercopithecus aethiops* (guenon monkey) and *Papio hamadryas* (sacred baboon), members of Cercopithecidae family; *Pongo pygmaeus* (orang-utan), member of Pongidae family; all of suborder Anthropoidea ("manlike" mammals) of order Primates.

LEXICON. *Hebrew:* QOPH.

deal of interest was shown in various types of apes. In Egyptian graves there are depictions of the baboon and the guenon. The Assyrians pictured the orang-utan, while in India apes were worshiped. King Solomon probably acquired apes to provide amusement in his court.

In stately calm this sacred baboon gazes out at the world. Modeled by an Egyptian sculptor in faïence (a kind of pottery), he dates from about 600 B.C., some three centuries after the reign of King Solomon in Israel. (Photograph courtesy of the Metropolitan Museum of Art. From the Carnarvon Collection; gift of Edward S. Harkness, 1926.)

The Ass

From earliest times the ass has been one of the most useful domestic animals in the Near East, while its introduction into Europe (Greece and Italy) came relatively late. It should be pointed out, though, that the animal referred to in the Bible was considerably different from the now familiar donkey of the West. Our donkeys are usually quite small, and are obstinate and rather mean animals that (not without reason) are accused of being stupid. But in warmer climates this animal develops into a large, pretty, and stately animal. In Egypt, for instance, donkeys used for riding can be as much as four and a half feet high, and are slender, speedy animals. Sometimes they are entirely white in color, but ordinarily the color of the Near Eastern ass is tawny, varying from lighter to darker shades. In fact, the Hebrew name for the ass, *chamor*, literally means "tawny"; Deborah challenges those

---

CLASSIFICATION. *Equus asinus,* member of Equidae family of order Perissodactyla (odd-toed hoofed mammals).

LEXICON. *Hebrew:* CHAMOR, ATHON. Also, AYIR (young ass, colt, foal); ARAD, AROD, or PERE (wild ass). *Greek:* ONOS. Also, ONARION or POLOS (colt, foal); HUPOZUGION (ass of burden).

"who ride on tawny asses" to join in the praise of God for the victory that has been won (Judg. 5:10). It is no accident then that biblical authors never mention the stubbornness, the meanness, or the laziness that we associate with the word "ass." These are traits that a Near Easterner would never see in this animal.

THE ASS AND ITS COUSIN

The ass is not, to be sure, as swift as the horse; but then, it has a great deal more endurance than its cousin, and the rider of an ass may cover just as much ground in the course of a day as the rider of a horse. In mountainous terrain the ass is much to be preferred over the horse because it has a much surer gait than the horse on narrow and difficult pathways. The ass also gets along much better in hot weather, and the drier the climate is, the better it likes it. Apparently a very frugal beast, it eats grass, hay, thistles, and thorny twigs —all with equally good appetite. Its only demand is that its drinking water be clean.

THE RIDING ASS

From the time of the patriarchs on, the ass is frequently referred to in the Bible as a riding and pack animal. The she-ass was much preferred to the male as a riding animal, and in earliest times, the ass was the only riding animal used, even by distinguished personages and war heroes; for example, the thirty sons of Jair the Gileadite (Judg. 10:4) and Abdon's forty sons and thirty grandsons (Judg. 12:14) all rode on asses. Asses were used in warfare throughout the history of the Near East, although in the time of David the mule came into favor, and in Solomon's time, after the Egyptian pattern, the horse became dominant. Nevertheless, asses continued to be used militarily outside of Israel, and we read about them in connection with the Syrians (II Kings 7:7-10) and the Medes (Isa. 21:7).

A charioteer proudly guides his matched team of donkeys in this reconstructed model of a copper object dating from 2800 B.C. in Sumeria, later known as Babylon. Horses were not used for such warlike activities until the time of Solomon, almost two millennia later. (Photograph courtesy of the Oriental Institute of the University of Chicago.)

A doleful donkey carefully treads the path to Jerusalem bearing the Prince of Peace in this medieval depiction of Palm Sunday. The artist shows how garments were used as a saddle, faithfully following the text, although Jerusalem appears to be a medieval castle. The illustration is a detail from the Huntingfield Psalter, dating from the thirteenth century. (Photograph courtesy of the Pierpont Morgan Library.)

Women in biblical times often used the ass as a riding animal, as for example, Achsah the wife of Othniel (Josh. 15:18), Abigail (I Sam. 25:23), and the Shunammite woman (II Kings 4:24). Often a special driver would help the woman guide her beast, running ahead of or at the side of the animal. If a married couple possessed only one donkey, the husband usually walked alongside while the wife rode; thus Moses took "his wife and his sons and set them on an ass, and went back to the land of Egypt" (Exod. 4:20). Although no description is given in the Bible, artists usually depict the flight of the holy family into Egypt in this fashion.

The riding ass never lost its popularity for everyday use in

Israel, and thus it was that a man riding upon an ass became a symbol of the Prince of Peace: "Lo, your king comes to you; triumphant and victorious is he, humble and riding on an ass, on a colt the foal of an ass" (Zech. 9:9). It was this prophecy that Jesus fulfilled as he rode into Jerusalem, and no Israelite could be in doubt about the nature of the kingdom he thus proclaimed: it was to be a kingdom of peace. As John explained in his Gospel: "And Jesus found a young ass and sat upon it; as it is written, 'Fear not, daughter of Zion; behold thy king is coming, sitting on an ass's colt!'" (John 12:14-15). The King would come riding on a common donkey.

No real saddle was used in riding an ass; a covering was merely tied onto its back and a halter affixed. This procedure is mentioned in the New Testament when the disciples prepared Jesus' mount for the entry into Jerusalem, except that, realizing the special nature of the occasion, the disciples did not want to use the ordinary covering for the donkey's back. Instead, they "put their garments" on it, and Jesus sat on these (Matt. 21:7).

MEASURE OF WEALTH

Throughout the Bible, then, the ass is regarded as an animal of considerable value. Abraham received numerous asses, both male and female, as gifts from Pharaoh (Gen. 12:16), to add to his already large stable. The wealthy Job had five hundred she-asses before catastrophe hit him (Job 1:3), and after his redemption possessed a thousand (Job 42:12). The ass was an excellent pack animal and is often referred to in the Bible as such; for example, Joseph's brothers used them to transport the grain they purchased in Egypt (Gen. 42:26; 45:23). The ass was always an important means for carrying food, as when Abigail transported "two hundred loaves, and two skins of wine, and five sheep already dressed, and five measures of parched grain, and a hundred clusters of raisins, and two hundred cakes of figs" to David, in order to feed him

and his troops during his conflict with Saul (I Sam. 25:18).
How important the she-asses were to David can be seen by
the fact that one of the twelve managers of his royal estates,
Jehdeiah the Meronothite, was assigned exclusively to look
after them (I Chron. 27:30).

"OX AND ASS"

During the time of Christ the phrase "ox and ass" was the
common way to refer to domestic animals in general (like
our word "livestock"). Jesus uses the phrase in this sense in
his words about the legality of healing on the Sabbath: "Does
not each of you on the sabbath untie his ox or his ass from
the manger, and lead it away to water it?" (Luke 13:15).
The ox and the ass are mentioned here, as they are in the
Tenth Commandment ("Thou shalt not covet thy neighbor's
. . . ox, nor his ass . . ."), to express what was ordinarily the
property of every Israelite.

A NOBLE NAME

Although the pack ass was a valuable piece of property,
it was not nearly as noble a creature as the riding ass. A
prince could bear the name "Hamor," meaning "ass," proudly
and without being degraded (Gen. 33:19), but there is a
touch of sarcasm in Jacob's words about his son Issachar,
meaning "strong ass," that is, a pack animal: he is described
as "crouching between the sheepfolds," and becoming "a
slave at forced labor" (Gen. 49:14-15). Some of the animals
were also used as draft animals—to pull plows and to turn
large millstones for the grinding of grain. The law of Moses
forbade the hitching of an ox and an ass to the same plow,
even though this practice may still be seen in parts of the
Near East. The large millstones were known as "ass millstones," and were widely used at the time of Jesus. There is
reference to one of these in a saying of Jesus: "But whoever
causes one of these little ones who believe in me to sin, it

would be better for him to have a great millstone [literally, 'ass millstone'] fastened round his neck and to be drowned in the depth of the sea" (Matt. 18:6; Luke 17:2).

The ass, unlike the ox, was worthless to an Israelite when it was killed, for its flesh was declared unclean in Mosaic law. Thus after its death it had to be dragged out and thrown away beyond the city gates. This end is what Jeremiah means when he says that King Jehoiakim of Judah will suffer the fate of "the burial of an ass" (Jer. 22:19). In times of extremity, some Israelites obviously broke the Mosaic law against eating donkey meat: during the Syrian siege of Samaria the famine was so severe that even the head of an ass was selling for eighty silver shekels (II Kings 6:25).

A TALKING DONKEY

One of the most famous incidents in the Bible involving an ass is the story of Balaam the prophet and his faithful riding donkey. Besides being the only incident in the Bible in which a mount speaks to its rider, it reveals in a very interesting manner the general character of the Near Eastern riding ass and the Israelites' idea of how these creatures were to be treated. According to Numbers 22, the donkey balked at the sight of the angel of the Lord blocking its path, but Balaam, unable to see the angel, thought his mount was being stubborn and began to beat it. The donkey was allowed to speak and berated Balaam for beating it, asking him if he had ever known it to act stubborn before. Balaam had to admit that he had not, at which time his eyes were opened, he could see and hear the angel, and he had all the more reason to regret his rash actions toward his beast. The angel told him that had the donkey not stopped, "surely just now I would have slain you and let her live." Two points about the donkey in the Near East are made clear here: first, it was seldom stubborn without good reason, and second, it was supposed to be treated with respect by its owner.

The Bat

The bat is a mammal, even though in the Pentateuch (Lev. 11:19; Deut. 14:18) it is listed with the unclean birds—the stork, the heron, and the hoopoe—as abominations that must not be eaten. The only mammal able to fly, it forms a biological order by itself. The order, Chiroptera, is divided into two suborders: large bats, which are fruit-eaters and are found only in the tropics and subtropics; and small bats, which are insect-eaters and are found wherever there are insects. Within these categories are about one thousand species and subspecies.

ABHORRENT . . .

The large bats prefer to live in inaccessible parts of the jungle. Here they may be found by the hundreds and thousands, hanging from tree branches like fruit. At twilight they leave their resting places and venture out into the dusk to seek food. They have very keen eyesight, a well-developed

---

CLASSIFICATION. Egyptian leaf-nosed bat, member of genus *Hipposideros*, suborder Microchiroptera of order Chiroptera (the bats).
LEXICON. *Hebrew:* ATALLEPH.

---

sense of feeling, and a sharp sense of smell, and so can move with amazing ease through the darkness to find trees and vines that bear juicy, ripe fruits. A swarm of bats can strip an orchard bare in a very short time, and are thus regarded as enemies and predators. These large bats reach a length of about eighteen inches, with a wing span of some fifty-four inches.

The small bats are only from two to six inches long, with a wing span of from eight to twenty-eight inches. Because they are insect-eaters, they are regarded as useful animals, but they are still abhorred by humans. In colder regions bats hibernate in the winter, but in many areas—such as the warm Dead Sea Valley in Palestine—they can be seen flying all year round.

. . . AND ODIOUS

The insect-eating small bats are found in old buildings in Jerusalem, in grottoes and caverns in Galilee, by the Sea of Galilee, and near the Dead Sea. One of the varieties in these regions is the Egyptian leaf-nosed bat, a light gray animal with a two-inch tail and a wing span of about eight inches. Incredible numbers of them can be found living in the same place, where their excrement forms thick layers at the bottom of their caves, giving off a most odious smell.

These bats are rightly regarded as loathsome and disgusting creatures. In Isaiah's picture of the Day of the Lord and the judgment of the ungodly, a particularly effective detail is his mention of the bat: "In that day men will cast forth their idols of silver and their idols of gold, which they made for themselves to worship, to the moles and to the bats, to enter the caverns of the rocks and the clefts of the cliffs, from before the terror of the Lord, and from the glory of his majesty, when he rises to terrify the earth" (Isa. 2:20-21). There could hardly be a more demeaning end for man's idols —once the object of worship and sacrifice—than to be "cast forth" among the bats in their caverns.

Pictured here in its natural position, hanging upside down from a tree limb, is one of the larger varieties of fruit-eating bats. This creature looks more like a mammal, and slightly less repulsive, than its insect-eating relative. (Photograph courtesy of the Chicago Natural History Museum.)

18

The Bear

The bear is a predatory animal that can be widely found on every continent except Australia (the so-called koala "bear" is really a marsupial) and Antarctica. Characteristics common to all varieties are the clumsy build, relatively short legs, the broad head with its cone-shaped nose, the short tail, and the large paws with bare soles. The bear, which is omnivorous (both flesh- and plant-eating), has sharp front teeth like the flesh-eating mammals and gnarled back teeth like the plant-eating mammals. As a result of its dependence on plant food, the bear retires to its lair during the winter. The length of its hibernation depends upon the severity of the winter. In spite of its clumsy build and great weight, the bear is agile and quick. With ease it travels across rocky slopes, swims rivers, and climbs trees. It can run at speeds of up to thirty miles per hour.

Of the well-known members of the bear family—the grizzly, the polar, the black, and the brown—only the brown bear is

---

CLASSIFICATION. *Ursus arctos* (European brown bear), member of Ursidae family of order Carnivora (flesh-eating mammals).
LEXICON. *Hebrew:* DOB. *Greek:* ARKTOS.

native to the Palestine area. Today it is found only in the Lebanon and Anti-Lebanon Mountains, and even there it is rare, but in antiquity it was found everywhere in Palestine. Named for its brown, tufted pelt, this species differs from its relatives in its prominently vaulted forehead and its very short paws with their long claws. The brown bear can grow up to six feet long and can weigh as much as five hundred pounds. Its food consists mainly of roots, grass, berries, fruits, leaves,

The ferocious mien of this charging bear makes one realize how great was the courage of David and how terrible the fate of the boys who taunted Elisha. This relief sculpture is from Mesopotamia a few centuries after the birth of Christ. (Photograph courtesy of the Metropolitan Museum of Art.)

nuts, honey, and ants, but it will also hunt deer, oxen, horses, and particularly sheep. At times it will even eat carrion.

FURY OF THE FEMALE

Bears rarely attack people. If a bear chances to encounter a human, it prefers to ignore him. Only when provoked or annoyed is a bear dangerous, particularly if it is a female with cubs. She is the protector of the family, and will defend her young in wild fury and with great courage. Her concern for her cubs is not only touching but necessary, for at birth they are blind and not much larger than rats. They cannot leave the lair until they are about three months old, and must remain with the mother for protection for two years, during which time she teaches them to hunt and protect themselves.

If the fury of the female bear defending her cubs is great, the fury of one who has lost a cub is all the more dangerous. Thus, we can fully understand the familiar biblical proverb on dealing with a fool: "Let a man meet a she-bear robbed of her cubs, rather than a fool in his folly" (Prov. 17:12). Hushai, advising Absalom not to pursue his father David, says: "You know that your father and his men are mighty men, and that they are enraged, like a bear robbed of her cubs in the field" (II Sam. 17:8).

LIKE A BEAR

The growl of a bear is a threatening sound; it expresses his dissatisfaction and impatience. At least this is how Isaiah interprets it when, confronting his countrymen with their own impatience, he likens sinful murmuring against God to the bear's growl: "We all growl like bears" (Isa. 59:11). A predatory animal as dangerous and feared as the bear could also, in the imagination of a biblical poet, become a picture of the military might of the great world powers, as in Daniel's dream vision of the kingdom of the Medes: "And behold, another beast, a second one, like a bear. It was raised up on one side;

21

it had three ribs in its mouth between its teeth; and it was told, 'Arise, devour much flesh'" (Dan. 7:5).

A blow from a bear's paw can be fatal, and the least it can do is to throw the victim off balance. Thus, David's heroic courage and strength as a young shepherd are shown in his claim before Saul that he had not hesitated to run after a bear and wrench from its jaws one of his father's sheep. And, as if that were not enough, David added: "If he arose against me, I caught him by his beard, and smote him and killed him" (I Sam. 17:34-35).

THE BEAR OR THE LION?

Bears and lions are often mentioned together in the Bible, because they were the two largest and strongest predatory animals known (for example, I Sam. 17:37). Which was the more dangerous was a moot question, one which the prophet Amos expresses as something like the difference between the frying pan and the fire. Warning those who are overanxious to see the Day of the Lord, he says: "Why would you have the day of the Lord? It is darkness, and not light; as if a man fled from a lion, and a bear met him" (Amos 5:18-19). On the whole, however, the bear seems to have the edge over the lion in biblical accounts, if only by dint of the bloody narrative involving the prophet Elisha (II Kings 2:23-24). On his way to Bethel the prophet met some small boys who made fun of him. "Go up, you baldhead! Go up, you baldhead!" they shouted. Elisha became angry, turned and cursed the boys, and immediately two she-bears came out from a thicket and tore them apart—forty-two boys in all.

This rather gruesome tale, which is undoubtedly without parallel in world literature, nevertheless typifies a common biblical treatment of animals: all of God's creatures must perform his errands. God would not tolerate the mocking of his prophet, and so the bears had to perform this bloodthirsty deed, although, as we know, it was contrary to their nature.

The Camel

Like the cow and other bovines, the camel is a ruminant, that is, it chews its cud, but it differs from them in having neither horns nor antlers. The camel referred to in the Bible is the single-humped dromedary, a slim, long-legged animal with a thick covering of hair, usually of a light, sandy color. On the head and the hump the hair is a little longer than elsewhere and somewhat bushy. The dromedary can grow up to seven feet tall, measuring as much as nine feet from its muzzle to the tip of its tail. The more obvious features of the camel, in addition to its hump, are its long, curved neck and its rather long head.

Nature has equipped the camel particularly well for desert living. The broad soles of its feet are furnished with elastic,

---

CLASSIFICATION. *Camelus dromedarius* (dromedary, or Arabian camel), *Camelus bactrianus* (Bactrian camel), members of Camelidae family of order Artiodactyla (even-toed hoofed mammals).

LEXICON. *Hebrew:* GAMAL. Also, KIRKAROTH or ACHASHTERANIM (dromedaries); BEKER or BIKRAH (young camel). *Greek:* KAMELOS.

23

hornlike pads; each foot has only two toes and no solid hoof (the hooflike formations at the end of the toes resemble ordinary toenails). Unlike other ungulates (hoofed creatures), the camel does not walk on the end toe-joint alone but on the last two. The inside walls of the camel's three-chambered stomach are lined with numerous cells that can hold from fifteen to thirty quarts of liquid, enabling the camel to go long periods without drinking—as much as five days during the summer and twenty-five days in the wintertime. Besides having this stomach reservoir, the camel can store food in its hump and so can also go without food for long periods of time. The hump is composed of fatty tissue, and the more food the camel gets, the larger the hump becomes. When the animal is in prime condition, the hump makes up one fourth of the back, but when

On the walls of Persepolis, the ancient city of Persia that was sacked by Alexander the Great, tribute-bearers are shown leading the two-humped camel. This beast, the Bactrian camel, is larger and heavier than its cousin the dromedary, with longer, thicker, and darker hair, which equips it better for colder climates. (Photograph courtesy of the Oriental Institute of the University of Chicago.)

the fatty deposit in the hump is being consumed it may shrink until it almost disappears.

The camel's nostrils are pinched together to form long fissures along the length of its head. These can be closed at will to prevent penetration of sand, especially during violent sandstorms. The upper lip hangs down over the lower, and both are thick and leather-like, enabling the camel to pick up the thistle and cactus that grow in the desert. The driest desert plants provide food for the camel; in an emergency a basket or a mat made of date palm leaves will do, and the beast will even eat acacia twigs, the thorns of which are so sharp they penetrate the sole of a man's shoe.

THE DESERT SHIP

The camel's nickname, "the desert ship," indicates how widely it is used as a riding and pack animal in desert regions. And truly it is indispensable there, for its frugal eating habits, its perseverance, and its strength are exactly what is needed in the wilderness. The history of the early Hebrews is closely tied to the desert, and it is no surprise to find the camel mentioned early in the narrative of Genesis. Among the gifts Egypt's Pharaoh bestows upon Abraham for the sake of his wife Sarah are mentioned camels (Gen. 12:16), although the writer is surely guilty of a small mistake here. Undoubtedly, a Palestinian would take it for granted that expensive gifts from a royal party would include camels, but the Egyptians simply could not do this in Abraham's time; it is fully established that there were no camels in Egypt before the time of the Persians, more than a millennium later. The father of the Israelite nation may not have received his camels from Egypt, but undoubtedly he had a large stable, for we read that when Abraham's servant traveled across the desert to the city of Nahor in Mesopotamia he brought with him "ten of his master's camels" laden with "all sorts of choice gifts" (Gen. 24:10).

Camels were common among the Israelites throughout their early history, as well as among their neighbors to the east, the Midianites, the Ishmaelites, and the Amalekites. These three nations were the real camel breeders. In the story of Gideon we read: "The Midianites and the Amalekites and all the people of the East lay along the valley like locusts for multitude; and their camels were without number, as the sand which is upon the seashore for multitude" (Judg. 7:12). Obviously, then, camels were used in warfare. War camels are also mentioned in the prophecy of Isaiah about the fall of Babylon (Isa. 21:7). Among the Arabs (Ishmaelites) the war camel was often mounted by two bowmen. The Persians Cyrus and Xerxes and the Syrian Antiochus the Great all had camel corps.

CAUSES SEASICKNESS

For riding through desert regions the camel has no match, but the inexperienced rider may suffer symptoms of seasickness, for the animal's ambling gait produces a slow, rocking motion. The experienced rider, however, can ride comfortably even without a saddle, leaning his elbows on his knees, and can even read while riding. A good riding camel can cover more than one hundred miles in a twelve-hour period and can trot for four days without respite. The camel saddles of ancient times, of which there were several designs, had some features in common: a wooden frame that was placed over the camel's hump, a pillow for the rider to sit on, and usually a pair of baskets or bags on the sides for baggage. For women and children a canopy was usually suspended over the saddle as protection against the sun. In the Pentateuch there is an account of an unusual use for the saddle. Rachel, after becoming Jacob's wife, stole her father's household gods—which may have resembled small dolls—and concealed them beneath her saddle as she rode off with her husband (Gen. 31:34).

Usually a camel rider dismounts by having the camel kneel,

"Drink, and I will water your camels," says Rebekah to the servant of Abraham, thus proving herself a likely candidate to become Isaac's wife (Genesis 24). This episode, as well as her trip to meet her future spouse, is depicted in this detail from a twelfth-century mosaic in the nave of the Monreale Cathedral in Italy. (Photograph by Anderson.)

but if necessary he can get down more quickly by sliding down a camel driver's rod leaned against the hump. This is perhaps what the young Rebekah did "when she saw Isaac" for the first time and "alighted from the camel" (Gen. 24:64). It is part of Oriental courtesy not to greet anyone from the back of a mount.

Rich men and powerful kings frequently had large herds of camels; for instance, Job had three thousand camels. A riding animal as useful and expensive as the camel would naturally be highly treasured by its owner. In order to ensure his camels the best of treatment, David appointed a native Ishmaelite— from a nation known for its skill with camels—as superintendent of his stable. The owner's joy and pride in possessing this valuable beast sometimes found expression in the practice of decorating the camel. The kings of Midian, for example, hung chains around the necks of their camels and decorated them with crescents (Judg. 8:21).

Pack camels naturally travel more slowly than the riding camels—about thirty miles a day. The camel's hump is very sensitive to pressure, so it must be loaded carefully. A padded

27

saddle is placed on it, and the load hangs down on both sides in order to distribute the weight. During the loading process the camel must lie down in its natural resting position—its legs folded under, its weight on its knees and elbows, which are covered with bare, hard skin-pads. Sometimes it is even necessary to tie the legs in this position while the camel is being loaded, for it is a temperamental beast that is often stubborn and seldom shows any affection toward its owner. A good pack camel can carry from three to five hundred pounds in a load. The prophet's picture of loaded pack camels thus embellishes his description of the sumptuous wealth of the future Jerusalem: "A multitude of camels shall cover you, the young camels of Midian and Ephah; all those from Sheba shall come. They shall bring gold and frankincense, and shall proclaim the praise of the Lord" (Isa. 60:6). The fabulous queen of Sheba used camels to carry the riches she brought with her to Solomon's court (I Kings 10:2). And when Hazael, following King Benhadad's orders, brought Elisha a gift from Damascus loaded on forty camels, the total weight of the valuables must have been some seventeen thousand pounds (II Kings 8:9).

TEST FOR A WIFE

When riding or pack camels reach their destination after a journey, their first needs are to be unloaded and then watered. Such is the scene described in the story of Abraham's servant, who had been sent out with ten camels loaded with gifts to find a wife for Isaac. After arriving in Nahor, "he made the camels kneel down outside the city by the well of water at the time of evening, the time when women go out to draw water" (Gen. 24:11). They still had to be watered, however, and the servant hit on a plan both to achieve that end and to find Isaac a wife. In his prayer he said: "Behold, I am standing by the spring of water, and the daughters of the men of the city are coming out to draw water. Let the maiden to whom

I shall say, 'Pray let down your jar that I may drink,' and who shall say, 'Drink, and I will water your camels'—let her be the one whom thou hast appointed for thy servant Isaac" (Gen. 24:13-14). In this way he could be sure of two things about the chosen maiden: first, she was kind and loving toward both man and beast, as well as knowledgeable about their needs; second, she was capable of doing the heavy work required of a nomadic wife. It was no small task to draw water for ten thirsty camels. The wells of that time were so constructed that in order to water animals a person had to walk down steps to reach the water and then carry it back up.

EXTREMELY USEFUL

The camel was an extremely useful domestic animal for the Israelites in many ways. Besides being used for transportation, it provided delicious milk. Its flesh can be eaten and is quite palatable, but Mosaic law forbade the Israelites to enjoy it (Lev. 11:4). The camel sheds its hair during early spring, and the hair is preserved and used in weaving cloth. The New Testament mentions that John the Baptist was clothed in camel's hair (Matt. 3:4; Mark 1:6). Even the camel's excrement was useful: when dried, it could be used as fuel.

Jesus makes mention of the camel twice, each time with wry humor. The first saying is well known: "It is easier for a camel to go through the eye of a needle than for a rich man to enter the kingdom of God" (Matt. 19:24). This comparison shows how difficult it is for a person to tear himself away from his earthly goods; we see a large, ungainly beast, confronted by a needle with its almost invisible eye. Another time, berating the Pharisees, Jesus used the same kind of comparison to describe the effect of their strict legalism. Referring to the practice of straining wine before it was drunk in order to remove impurities, Jesus said: "You blind guides, straining out a gnat and swallowing a camel!" (Matt. 23:24).

The Deer

At the present time deer are completely extinct in the Palestine area, but we have abundant evidence that they were plentiful there in biblical times. First, deer teeth and knucklebones have been found in Lebanon; there can be no question that deer existed in ancient Egypt; and there is also a picture of a hart and two does in the palace of Sennacherib, king of Assyria. Second, there are the two Israelite towns named Aijalon. One was a Levite town in the territory of Dan (Josh. 21:24); the other was in the territory of Zebulun (Judg. 12:12). This place name is derived from the Hebrew word for deer, *ayyal,* in much the same way as the English name Deerfield is derived from "deer." Finally, there are the considerable number of references to deer made by the biblical authors. It

---

CLASSIFICATION. Deer belong to the Cervidae family of the Pecora group (true ruminants) in the order Artiodactyla (even-toed hoofed mammals). Probable genus, *Cervus;* species unknown.

LEXICON. *Hebrew:* AYYAL. Also, AYYALAH, AYYELETH (hind); YAALAH (roe); YACHMUR (fallow deer).

---

should be noted, however, that there is no way to tell what genus of deer existed in Palestine; it is also quite possible that more than one variety was familiar to the different biblical writers.

In our English Bibles several different words are used to refer to the deer. The two most common words are "hart" and "hind." "Hart" refers to the adult male red deer, a species of large deer probably once found in Palestine and now common in temperate areas of Europe and Asia. The King James Version occasionally uses the word "stag" to refer to this deer, which is probably a mistranslation. The "hind" is the adult female of this species. "Doe," "roe," "roebuck," and "fallow deer" are terms used in only a few passages. "Doe," of course, is a general name for the female in any species in which the male is called a buck, other than the red deer, the moose, and the elk. "Roe" and "roebuck" are the female and male of the roe deer, a small, nimble European and Asiatic species (see the Appendix). The "fallow deer," a species smaller than the red deer, probably was one of the species found in Palestine in biblical times.

The Hebrews were permitted to eat the flesh of the deer, and that it was considered a great delicacy is suggested by the fact that King Solomon's sophisticated court kitchen was well supplied with venison (I Kings 4:23). However, the deer was forbidden for use as a sacrificial animal (Deut. 12:13-15).

A FAVORITE FIGURE

The deer receives special attention in the poetic and prophetic books of the Bible; what is impressive in these references is not only the poetic language used to describe this animal, but also the remarkable ability of the Hebrew authors to observe its characteristics and habits. They rejoiced at the sight of the deer's beauty and stately carriage, which turned their thoughts to heroes and kings. "God, the Lord, is my strength," says Habakkuk; "he makes my feet like the hinds' feet, he makes me tread upon my high places" (Hab. 3:19). In similar terms David gave thanks to the Lord for enabling him to be victorious over his enemies (II Sam. 22:34; cf. Ps. 18:33). In the Song of Solomon the bridegroom is compared to a "young stag upon rugged mountains" (Song of Sol. 2:17).

The deer's swiftness and sure-footedness was carefully observed and provides the background for one of the better-known passages in the Old Testament: "Then shall the lame man leap like a hart" (Isa. 35:6). Old Jacob's prophecy concerning the future of his sons includes the statement: "Naphtali is like a hind let loose" (Gen. 49:21). This saying could mean that the tribe of Naphtali is expected to be swift both in defense and in attack.

THE HIND

The hind especially impressed the Hebrew poets; with its dark, gentle eyes and graceful limbs, it was frequently used to describe the charm of a woman. Thus this advice to a husband: "Rejoice in the wife of your youth, a lovely hind, a graceful doe" (Prov. 5:18-19). One of the most dramatic passages in the Psalms gives us a powerful description of a thunderstorm in which "the voice of the Lord flashes forth flames of fire," "shakes the wilderness," "strips the forest bare" and "makes the hinds to calve" in the midst of the storm (Ps. 29:9, alternate reading).

Perhaps the most extensive observation of the life and habits of the deer is to be found in Job, where God is making clear to Job that He is the creator of nature and its wonders: "Do you observe the calving of the hinds? Can you number the months that they fulfil, and do you know the time when they bring forth, when they crouch, bring forth their offspring, and are delivered of their young? Their young ones become strong, they grow up in the open; they go forth, and do not return to them" (Job 39:1-4).

The hind normally gives birth to one calf at a time, after a gestation period of about forty weeks. When it is about to give birth it looks for a secure hiding place, preferably in the dense undergrowth of the forest where it can find natural protection for the tiny calf. During the first few days after birth the mother never goes far from her young. The solicitous care of the hind for her calf during the first days of its life is hinted at in a touching way in Jeremiah's description of a drought so terrible that "the ground . . . is dismayed" and "the farmers are ashamed, they cover their heads," and "even the hind in the field forsakes her newborn calf because there is no grass" (Jer. 14:4-5). It would be a terrible drought indeed that brought about such an unnatural desertion.

AS A HART LONGS . . .

The most familiar Scripture passage referring to the deer is undoubtedly the following quotation from the Psalms: "As a hart longs for flowing streams, so longs my soul for thee, O God" (Ps. 42:1). The Hebrew word for "longs" is sometimes translated as "languishes," "gasps," or "hangs out its tongue," for it really means "leans or reaches out" for something. The passage thus becomes even more effective when we know that the deer suffers from thirst much more than most other ruminants and shows its thirst by letting its tongue hang out. Through his careful observation of nature, the poet has successfully dramatized his intense thirst for spiritual refreshment. The picture is especially meaningful in a country where droughts during the hot summer months hit both man and beast very hard. During such times a deer could find water only in certain places in the wilderness, but would often stray far away from these places; likewise, the poet can find his spiritual refreshment only in the holy place in Zion, and he is far away from Zion as he writes this psalm.

The Dog

In antiquity the dog was not man's closest friend and constant companion—at least not in Israel—and the descriptions of the dog given in the Bible are of vagrant, half-wild, homeless animals. That they are mentioned some forty times by biblical authors is only an indication that they were a familiar part of everyday life.

The dogs common in Palestine apparently looked like the German Shepherd dog of today, with short pointed ears, a pointed nose, and a long and lightly bushy tail. From the Bible we get the impression that the dogs were attached to villages rather than to any particular house or family; that is, they belonged to the community as a whole, living and sleeping on the village streets. Throughout the day they slept in the sun, and were stirred into activity only when a strange dog strayed into their vicinity—in which case they would go after it until it retreated or had been torn to pieces. Strange people arriving in a village were also met by baying dogs, but familiar people were ignored. Thus, in the story of the

---

CLASSIFICATION. *Canis familiaris,* member of Canidae family (wolves, true dogs, jackals, and foxes) of order Carnivora (flesh-eating mammals).

LEXICON. *Hebrew:* KELEB. *Greek:* KUON. Also, KUNARION (little dog).

Exodus, the point is made that during the tenth plague the Israelites would be known to the angel of death and be passed over: "Against any of the people of Israel, either man or beast, not a dog shall growl" (Exod. 11:7).

PROWLING SCAVENGERS

With approaching darkness each evening the dogs would begin to roam about, howling and baying, in search of food. An Old Testament poet uses this trait as a sinister illustration of his ferocious enemies: "Each evening they come back, howling like dogs and prowling about the city" (Ps. 59:14). The dogs leaped greedily at anything edible, including refuse thrown out from the houses. In those days there was no such thing as a garbage collection; when the Israelites were commanded that they must not eat flesh from animals that had been "torn by beasts in the field" but must "cast it to the dogs" (Exod. 22:31), it was the same as if they had been told to throw it in the garbage can. Dogs would even eat carrion; in this respect they were like swine, with whom Jesus paired them in his saying: "Do not give dogs what is holy; and do not throw your pearls before swine" (Matt. 7:6).

Human corpses, too, could become the spoil of dogs. There was no greater infamy than that a dead body should lie unburied and become the prey of wild animals and dogs. This fate befell the wicked Queen Jezebel: "When they went to bury her, they found no more of her than the skull and the feet and the palms of her hands" (II Kings 9:35). Thus the dog served the same function as the vulture and other birds of prey. When the prophets wanted to speak about a threatening disaster, they conjured up a picture of dogs feeding on corpses; for example, when Ahijah predicted the extermination of the house of Jeroboam, he said: "Any one belonging to Jeroboam who dies in the city the dogs shall eat" (I Kings 14:11). The same fate overtook the families of Baasha and Ahab. One can easily understand, then, the mood of the

35

psalmist, who, feeling himself deserted in his loneliness and surrounded by dangers on all sides, compares himself to a solitary wanderer arriving in a strange village and being met by a pack of these half-wild dogs: "Yea, dogs are round about me; a company of evildoers encircle me" (Ps. 22:16). But even dogs were obliged to do the Lord's errands; according to Jeremiah, they were appointed to destroy apostates (Jer. 15:3).

"AM I A DOG . . ."

It is no wonder that "dog" was an invective in the mouth of a Hebrew. "Am I a dog, that you come to me with sticks?" the Philistine giant asked David (I Sam. 17:43; cf. II Sam. 3:8). Shime-i, who had cursed David, was greeted by Abishai with these words: "Why should this dead dog curse my lord the king? Let me go over and take off his head" (II Sam. 16:9). As a parallel to this meaning, a person who wanted to humble himself and give expression to deep submission called himself "dog"; Jonathan's son Mephibosheth, having

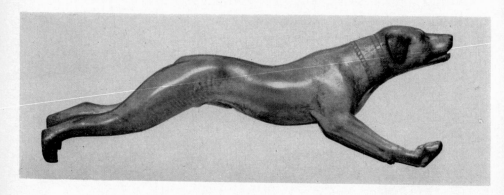

Although the Israelites had a low opinion of dogs, their neighbors the Egyptians were quite fond of them, going so far as to worship them. That they found dogs entertaining as well is revealed by this ivory toy from the Eighteenth Dynasty showing a hound in full cry; its lower jaw could even be moved up and down as if it were baying. (Photograph courtesy of the Metropolitan Museum of Art; Rogers Fund, 1940.)

been shown mercy by David, said: "What is your servant, that you should look upon a dead dog such as I?" (II Sam. 9:8; cf. I Sam. 24:14; II Kings 8:13). And Job described his misery similarly: "But now they make sport of me, men who are younger than I, whose fathers I would have disdained to set with the dogs of my flock" (Job 30:1). As an expression of the Lord's disapproval of the sacrifices of the godless, Isaiah said: "He who sacrifices a lamb [is] like him who breaks a dog's neck" (Isa. 66:3), that is, his sacrifices were worth no more than a dead dog. In Ecclesiastes the thought that life even in the lowliest state is better than death is expressed: "A living dog is better than a dead lion" (Eccles. 9:4).

GENERAL UNATTRACTIVENESS

The uncleanliness and general unattractiveness of the dog are mentioned in the New Testament to emphasize a writer's disgust. The author of the Second Letter of Peter, for instance, uses Prov. 26:11 to describe the abomination of false doctrines: "It has happened to them according to the true proverb, The dog turns back to his own vomit" (II Pet. 2:22). In the letter to the Philippians also the name "dog" is applied to false teachers (Phil. 3:2). Revelation declares that the dogs must stay outside the city gates where the sorcerers, fornicators, murderers, and idolaters are (Rev. 22:15).

Later Judaism referred to the gentiles as "dogs." In accordance with this common usage, Jesus said to the gentile woman from the district of Tyre and Sidon: "It is not fair to take the children's [that is, the Jewish people's] bread and throw it to the dogs" (Matt. 15:26; Mark 7:27). But the word he used for "dogs" has a mild sound (literally, "little dogs"), and does not carry the same scorn that was generally conveyed by "dog." The woman replied: "Even the dogs eat the crumbs that fall from their master's table" (Matt. 15:27; Mark 7:28), suggesting that dogs were then kept in the home.

There is one characteristic of the dog that the Jews learned

37

to appreciate—its watchfulness. Shepherds thus made use of dogs to give alarm when thieves or wild animals were approaching during the night. But these dogs were not trained, as they are now, to keep the flock together. When Isaiah compared the godless leaders of his people to "dumb dogs" (Isa. 56:10), he was saying that these leaders were as useless as dogs that do not bark at danger.

The Fox

"Foxes have holes, and birds of the air have nests; but the Son of man has nowhere to lay his head." This warning Jesus gave to the scribe who wished to become his follower (Matt. 8:20), and in doing so he mentioned one of the most common predatory animals in Palestine, the fox, whose holes could be found everywhere—most often in barren, deserted places, but also near vineyards.

Two kinds of foxes are extant in Palestine. The Egyptian fox, found in the central and southern parts of the country, is somewhat smaller than the common red fox. Its back is rust colored and its belly white. The Syrian fox, which lives

---

CLASSIFICATION. *Vulpes niloticus* (Egyptian fox), *Vulpes flavescens* (Syrian fox), members of Canidae family (wolves, true dogs, jackals, and foxes) of order Carnivora (flesh-eating mammals).

LEXICON. *Hebrew:* SHUAL. *Greek:* ALOPEX.

in the northern region of the Holy Land, is a shiny golden color.

WILY AND SLY

The fox rarely turns up its nose at any kind of food; it eats fruit, plants, mice, beetles, leverets, and birds with equally good appetite, but it seldom touches carrion. Its well-developed sense of smell makes it an excellent hunter, and it can approach its victim with great cunning and skill. We have come to consider the fox wily and sly, and Jesus probably had these characteristics in mind during his conversation with the Pharisees about Herod. Jesus had been warned: "Get away from here, for Herod wants to kill you," and he answered: "Go and tell that fox, 'Behold, I cast out demons and perform cures . . .'" (Luke 13:31-32). Apparently he recognized in Herod the cunning and rapacity, the cravenness and caution, with which a fox hunts its prey.

Another undesirable trait of this animal is implied in the well-known line in the Song of Solomon: "Catch us the foxes, the little foxes, that spoil the vineyards" (Song of Sol. 2:15). Not only does the fox love the sweet juice of the grape, but it also burrows underground tunnels that can destroy the vines. The Ammonites, who ridiculed the effort of the Jews to rebuild the walls around Jerusalem, referred to the fox's habit of digging its holes in old ruins when they said scornfully: "Yes, what are they building—if a fox goes up on it he will break down their stone wall!" (Neh. 4:3).

SAMSON'S FEAT

The most foxes ever to appear at one time in any of the narratives in the Bible are in the story of Samson. The Israelite hero caught three hundred of them, turned them tail to tail, and attached a torch to each pair of tails. When he had lit the torches, he released the foxes into the standing grain of the Philistines and "burned up the shocks and the standing

The alertness, if not the legendary craftiness, of the fox is evident in this picture of the red fox (*Vulpes fulva*), a close relative of the species native to the Holy Land. (Photograph courtesy of the Chicago Natural History Museum.)

grain, as well as the olive orchards" (Judg. 15:4-5). The collecting of all these foxes was certainly one of Samson's mightiest feats, for foxes, unlike their gregarious cousins the jackals, are never found in groups. Thus Samson had to track them down diligently one by one. Of course, it could be that the creatures were actually jackals, since the Hebrew word *shual* is sometimes used to refer to the jackal.

The Goat

The goat is a hollow-horned, cud-chewing mammal (ruminant) belonging to the order of the "cloven-hoofed" mammals (Artiodactyla). It is a powerfully built creature with relatively short legs and a stubby, triangular tail that is bare on the underside and usually points straight up. Its eyes are large and expressive, and its big, floppy ears constantly twitch. Horns and a beard, or "goatee," are characteristic features of the goat. The backward-arching horns, frequently with their points turned outward, are common to both males and females. Domesticated goats can have as many as four kids in one litter, while wild goats bear only one or two. The defenselessness of the newborn goat is mentioned by Isaiah in describing the kingdom of God: "And the leopard shall lie down with the kid" (Isa. 11:6).

The favorite habitat of wild goats is in inaccessible moun-

CLASSIFICATION. *Capra mambrica,* member of Bovidae family of order Artiodactyla (even-toed hoofed mammals).

LEXICON. *Hebrew:* EZ (goat or she-goat). Also, ATTUD, TSAPHIR, or TAYISH (he-goat); SAIR or SEIRAH (goat or kid); GEDI, GEDIYYAH, or BENE IZZIM (kid); YEELIM (wild goats). *Greek:* TRAGOS (he-goat). Also, ERIPHOS or ERIPHION (kid); DERMA AIGEION (goatskin).

tain regions, where the lively, playful animals live together in flocks—for the goat is a gregarious creature—and feed on mountain vegetation. They have an astounding ability to travel along a very narrow rock ledge or the brink of a steep precipice. In sure-footedness the wild goat is surpassed only by the chamois, one of its close relatives.

LEADING HE-GOAT

Domesticated goats usually graze in small flocks on hillside pastures. To one Israelite chronicler the army of Israel looked like "two little flocks of goats" when it won a victory over the Syrians, defeating an enemy that "filled the country" (I Kings 20:27). When goats are grazing they follow their leader, usually an older male goat that steps solemnly ahead of the rest of the flock as soon as they are let out of the stable or fold. This sight impressed one Hebrew proverbist enough so that he compared it with the leadership of royalty: "Four are stately in their stride: the lion, which is mightiest among beasts and does not turn back before any; the strutting cock, the he-goat, and a king striding before his people" (Prov. 30:29-31). And when Jeremiah predicted the return from Babylon he described the triumphal homecoming of the people thus: "Flee from the midst of Babylon, and go out of the land of the Chaldeans, and be as he-goats before the flock" (Jer. 50:8). "He-goats" is also used as a name for the leaders of Israel whom the Lord would punish if they betrayed his trust: "My anger is hot against the shepherds, and I will punish the he-goats" (Zech. 10:3, alternate reading).

A CONSPICUOUS HORN

In the book of Daniel there is described a he-goat that "came from the west across the face of the whole earth, without touching the ground; and the goat had a conspicuous horn between his eyes" (Dan. 8:5). This prophetic vision is interpreted as a symbol of Alexander the Great and his

This picturesque creature, fashioned out of gold by an ancient Mesopotamian artisan, originally was used to hold a tabletop; it is nevertheless a striking portrayal of a goat eating the bark off a tree. (Photograph courtesy of the University Museum, Philadelphia.)

Macedonian army. Apparently Daniel had in mind the belli-
cose nature of the male goat, which would aptly express the
victorious Alexander's uncontainable lust for power and
conquest.

A BELLIGERENT BEAST

It is quite possible that one of the common names for the
male goat in Hebrew, *ez* (derived from the root *azaz,* which
means "to be strong," "to be aggressive," or "to be impudent"),
is a reference to the creature's belligerence. This trait of the
goat often caused suffering for the weaker and more placid
sheep, which grazed with the goats, and a wise shepherd
always took care to keep them separated. The well-known
words of Jesus about the Last Judgment would be easily
understood in this sense by his rural-minded listeners: "As
a shepherd separates the sheep from the goats" so those who
are "blessed of my Father" will be separated from those who
are "cursed" (Matt. 25:32, 34, 41).

This undesirable characteristic notwithstanding, the goat
was an important part of the animal husbandry of the Hebrews throughout their history. The patriarchs of the Old
Testament all kept goats among their flocks. When Jacob,
after his years away from home, returned and was about to
meet his brother Esau, he chose as a gift for him "two hundred she-goats and twenty he-goats" (Gen. 32:14). It would
appear from this statement that one male was kept for every
ten females in the flock.

HIGHLY VALUED

Goats were highly valued because their flesh, their milk,
and their wool were all in general use. The flesh of male kids,
especially, was a much-favored food. For instance, when
Jacob had wanted to ingratiate himself with his father in order
to steal Esau's inheritance, he selected "two good kids" from
which his mother Rebekah prepared "savory food" for Isaac,

"such as he loves" (Gen. 27:9). And when Samson visited his wife in Timnah at the time of the wheat harvest, he brought with him a kid (Judg. 15:1). Jesse sent along a kid as a present for King Saul on the occasion of David's visit to his court (I Sam. 16:20). The elder brother in Christ's parable of the prodigal son complains that he has never been given a kid "that I might make merry with my friends" (Luke 15:29). Generally it was only the males that were used for food, and we may take it for granted that they fetched a good price in the market, an assumption supported by the prudent advice of Proverbs that a man give attention to his herds so that he may get for his goats "the price of a field" (Prov. 27:26). Goats are also mentioned in the list of Tyre's important trade goods for the world market (Ezek. 27:21).

Goats' milk, a great favorite as a beverage (Prov. 27:27), was also used in cooking meat and provided satisfaction for the gourmet palates of the time. Mosaic law, however, prohibited the boiling of a kid in its mother's milk (Exod. 23:19; 34:26; Deut. 14:21). The explanation of this curious rule has been sought in parallel commandments: for instance, it was regarded by the law as an unnatural cruelty to slaughter an animal and her young on the same day (Lev. 22:28; Deut. 22:6).

SILKY BLACK HAIR

The variety of goat most common in Palestine today is the *Capra mambrica,* which has long, floppy ears and a thick growth of long, silky black hair. In all probability this goat or a quite similar animal is the one the ancient Israelites knew. Black goats with white spots apparently were quite rare. At least Rachel's father, Laban, whose generosity was not overwhelming, readily agreed to Jacob's proposal as to how his salary was to be determined: "Let me pass through all your flock today, removing from it . . . the spotted and speckled among the goats; and such shall be my wages" (Gen. 30:32).

Appropriately enough, this detail from a relief portraying the Last Judgment was carried on the sarcophagus of a fourth-century Christian, in anticipation of the Shepherd who will separate the sheep from the goats, to the distinct advantage of the former. (Photograph courtesy of the Metropolitan Museum of Art; Rogers Fund, 1924.)

Of course Jacob had devised a plan to make his wages worthwhile—a highly unusual plan by modern standards, but one which nevertheless worked for him (see "The Sheep," pp. 104-106).

With its long black hair the goat was appropriate subject matter for poets, and the author of the Song of Solomon compared the black locks billowing down the shoulders of his beloved to a flock of goats encamped on a mountain ridge: "Behold, you are beautiful, my love, behold, you are beautiful! . . . Your hair is like a flock of goats, moving down the slopes of Gilead" (Song of Sol. 4:1; 6:5). Goats' hair could actually be mistaken for human hair, a fact which Michal capitalized on when she made possible the escape of her husband David. She took the household idol and "laid it on the bed and put a pillow of goats' hair at its head, and covered it with the clothes" (I Sam. 19:13). Saul's soldiers fell for the ruse, thinking the dummy was David, and he had time to make his getaway. The goats'-hair "pillow" was probably a piece of woven material used as protection against mosquitoes and flies.

JACOB'S RUSE

Another successful ruse in which goats' hair played a role was when Jacob covered his arms and neck with it to persuade his father Isaac, whose sight was failing, that he was the hairy Esau and should therefore receive the paternal blessing and the birthright (Gen. 27:1-41). First his mother Rebekah prepared "savory food" from two kids, and then "the skins of the kids she put upon his [Jacob's] hands and upon the smooth part of his neck" (Gen. 27:16). Isaac was suspicious, or at least confused, for he said: "The voice is Jacob's voice, but the hands are the hands of Esau" (Gen. 27:22). He even asked: "Are you really my son Esau?" (Gen. 27:24). But Isaac did give Jacob the blessing, convinced by his hairy hands and neck. This trick was discovered as soon as Esau showed up to receive the blessing himself. Isaac had to tell him: "Your brother came with guile, and he has taken away your blessing" (Gen. 27:35).

The shearing of goats took place in late spring. Goats' hair was not of the same commercial value as sheep's wool, but was particularly important in the weaving of tent cloth, for the long goats' hair could be spun into a tough, durable twine. The covenant tent at Mount Sinai was made of goats'-hair blankets (Exod. 26:7), and Paul, of course, used this material in his tentmaking trade. The material was generally black, like the hair itself: "I am very dark, but comely, O daughters of Jerusalem, like the tents of Kedar, like the curtains of Solomon" (Song of Sol. 1:5).

Goats' hair and skins were used for clothing only in exceptional cases. Goatskins were an inadequate garment even for the poor, the author of the letter to the Hebrews seems to suggest in his description of the sufferings of the martyrs: "They were stoned, they were sawn in two, they were killed with the sword; they went about in skins of sheep and goats, destitute, afflicted, ill-treated . . ." (Heb. 11:37). Mourning garments, for those who dressed in "sackcloth and ashes," were made from black goats' hair, since mourning dress had to be primitive and uncomfortable. A loin cloth or sack made of the hair was bound around the waist or hips by means of a belt; it was worn next to the skin, under the outer clothing, and could not be removed even at night. A king, however, was permitted to avoid some of the discomfort and wear his goats'-hair garment on the outside, in place of a cape (Jonah 3:6).

OFFERING BY FIRE

Finally, it should be mentioned that the goat was an important sacrificial animal under the Old Covenant. After a kid passed the age of one week, it was usable for this purpose. Before then it had to remain with its mother, but "from the eighth day on it shall be acceptable as an offering by fire to the Lord" (Lev. 22:27). The goat was used as a thank offering, for the Passover, as a private burnt offering, as a sin offering for both leaders and private individuals, and on the great Day of the Atonement.

Thus we see that the goat entered significantly into every part of Hebrew life, not only providing meat, drink, and shelter, but also entering into their spiritual life.

The Hare

Not to be confused with the common rabbit, which belongs to a different genus and has relatively short ears and hind legs, the hare is what people in the United States call the "jack rabbit." Two varieties of the hare—and there are many throughout the world—are found in Palestine, the *Lepus syriacus* and the *Lepus judaea*. The former lives in wooded and inhabited regions; it looks quite a bit like the common hare of Europe, but has shorter ears and a broader head. The latter is somewhat smaller than the *syriacus*, but has longer ears. It lives in barren regions.

A SPIRITUAL CRISIS

In the Bible the hare is mentioned only in the Mosaic laws on unclean animals. This reference is rather well known because it was one of the passages that some of the earlier critics of the "infallibility of the Bible" loved to discuss. In this passage the hare is referred to as a ruminant: "And the hare, because it chews the cud but does not part the hoof, is unclean to you" (Lev. 11:6). When these critics learned from

CLASSIFICATION. *Lepus syriacus* and *Lepus judaea,* members of the Leoporidae family of order Lagomorpha (hares and rabbits).
LEXICON. *Hebrew:* ARNEBETH.

biologists that the hare does not chew its cud, they had an obvious "biblical error" to cast in the faces of those who held that the Bible was "the whole truth and nothing but the truth," right down to the punctuation marks. This one short sentence in the Mosaic dietary laws caused many a spiritual crisis when it first gained notoriety.

Most Christians today would say that one's belief in the Bible as the Word of God does not mean that every word in this book has eternal validity, since it contains many things not concerned with salvation. What makes it the "book of books" for a Christian is his belief that in the Bible God reveals his love for sinful men and shows them the way of salvation, Jesus Christ. In any case, only the foolhardy regard it as an encyclopedia in which one looks under "H" in a concordance to find adequate zoological information about the hare.

KEEN OBSERVERS

Nevertheless, anyone who studies the biblical descriptions of animal life will appreciate that the biblical writers had keen eyes and outstanding powers of observation. The "error" concerning the hare was probably due to this keen observation, uninformed by what naturalists later discovered by means of dissection. For the hare does possess a characteristic that many hunters have had occasion to observe, namely, when it is resting it moves its lips from side to side just like the ruminants. A seventeenth-century physician, Thomas Bartholin, believed that the hare was a ruminant until he dissected one; much to his surprise, he found that the hare had only one simple stomach. How could it be a ruminant, then? Reluctant to doubt the words of the Bible, he proposed a theory that another part of the hare's anatomy might serve the function of the ruminant's complex stomach.

More recent zoological investigations have brought out an interesting sequel to this centuries-old argument. Experiments with rabbits have shown that they produce two kinds of excrement: the ordinary kind, by which the organism relieves itself of waste, and the so-called "stomach balls." When these stomach balls leave the intestines, the animal catches them in its mouth, chews and swallows them, and they pass through the alimentary canal a second time, this time to be discarded as ordinary excrement. Thus, according to zoologists themselves, the hare "chews the cud but does not part the hoof," at least in a manner of speaking.

Apparently unaware that later in its history it will cause major disputes about the veracity of the Bible, the hare in this Egyptian wall painting from the Twelfth Dynasty seems far more concerned about its immediate future. Note the extremely long ears that differentiate the hare from the rabbit. The creatures in the other cage are hedgehogs. (Photograph courtesy of the Metropolitan Museum of Art.)

The Hippopotamus

"Behold, Behemoth, which I made as I made you; he eats grass like an ox. Behold, his strength in his loins, and his power in the muscles of his belly. He makes his tail stiff like a cedar; the sinews of his thighs are knit together. His bones are tubes of bronze, his limbs like bars of iron.

"He is the first of the works of God; let him who made him bring near his sword! For the mountains yield food for him where all the wild beasts play. Under the lotus plant he lies, in the covert of the reeds and in the marsh. For his shade the lotus trees cover him; the willows of the brook surround him. Behold, if the river is turbulent he is not frightened; he is confident though Jordan rushes against his mouth. Can one take him with hooks, or pierce his nose with a snare?" (Job 40:15-24).

We can well understand that this huge, odd creature, which can attain a length of more than twelve feet and weigh more than a ton, is presented in Job as a demonstration of God's creative power. This description is part of God's second speech to Job out of the whirlwind, in which Job is given to under-

---

CLASSIFICATION. *Hippopotamus amphibius*, member of Hippopotamidae family of order Artiodactyla (even-toed hoofed mammals).
LEXICON. *Hebrew:* BEHEMOTH.

stand that he has no right to demand an accounting of a God who can create such a marvel as the hippopotamus.

"BEHEMOTH"

The hippopotamus gave Bible interpreters of the past a great deal of trouble. The Hebrew word *behemoth* was explained by some to mean the elephant; others suggested the wild ox, the mammoth, or just a large animal-in-general. The masterly description in Job, with its many details about the beast's anatomy and behavior, leaves no doubt but that the animal is the hippopotamus. The word *behemoth* is thus not to be understood as the plural of *behemah*, meaning "beast," but is formed from the Egyptian name for the hippopotamus, *p-ehe-mau*, meaning "river buffalo." (Our word "hippopotamus" comes from the Greek and means "river horse," but there is little that is horselike about this creature.)

The massive head of the hippo is almost square. Its highly developed sense organs are so arranged that when the creature is in the water it can see, hear, and smell everything and hardly be noticed. Eyes and nostrils are located on small elevations so that, along with the ears, they remain almost imperceptible above the surface of the water while the rest of the animal is hidden underneath. The mouth, covered completely by the larger upper lip, is broad, with protruding teeth that can reach the incredible length of twenty-eight inches. The neck is short and thick, and the body is bulbous, with a belly so huge that when its owner walks across muddy terrain it drags and leaves a deep furrow in the mud. Its legs are disproportionately short, but massive and strong, and its feet have four hoofed toes connected by webs. The tail reaches almost to the ground, and is covered with bristles. The inch-thick hide is charcoal brown in color and smooth.

The hippopotamus prefers to be in the water. There the animal that looks so clumsy on land moves with great speed and agility. It frequently drifts along with the current with only

"Behold, Behemoth. . . ." An Egyptian artist of the Twelfth
Dynasty fashioned a model of the fearsome *p-ehe-mau*, the
hippopotamus, out of faïence and decorated it with the plants
and flowers of the hippo's natural habitat, the river. This object
was found in the tomb of Senbi, at Meir in the Nile Valley.
(Photograph courtesy of the Metropolitan Museum of Art; gift
of Edward S. Harkness, 1917.)

eyes, ears, and nostrils held alertly above the water's surface.
If danger approaches it dives and swims noiselessly underwater, to come to the surface in a different place. Before
emerging the hippo shoots a jet of water about three feet in
the air, and then, snorting and grunting and emitting a muffled
roar that sounds as though it were coming from the bottom
of a barrel, the hippo breaks the surface of the water, looking

like a prehistoric monster. The frightening roar of the hippopotamus makes all other wild animals silent.

The hippopotamus feeds on grasses and plants that it finds on river bottoms. Only if it does not find enough food does it come ashore. Here too, in spite of appearances, it can move with surprising ease, managing to climb high, steep river banks that a man could scramble up only with great effort. The hippo's visits ashore take place mostly at night, but when day comes it is easy to see where the beast has been: everything in its path has been trampled down and destroyed. To watch the hippopotamus eat is not a very pleasant experience. It has a prodigious appetite, and the lotus flowers along the banks of the Nile, plants growing on the river bottom, and everything green in sight disappear into the huge chasm of its mouth. If disturbed during its search for food, the hippo can be highly dangerous both to man and to other animals. Its thick hide easily repels even the sharpest spear or arrow, and its mammoth teeth enable it to kill human beings with ease.

HUNTED TO EXTINCTION

In former times the hippopotamus was found everywhere in Africa south of the Sahara and throughout the entire Nile Valley. According to the book of Job it existed also in the Jordan Valley. Today the hippo is extinct in Egypt, destroyed by hunters who sought the ivory of its teeth, its thick hide (from which were made, among other things, the infamous hippopotamus-skin whips), and its blubber and meat, a favorite food among the Egyptians. The dangers and difficulties of hunting the hippo were diligently overcome: the animals were pursued from the river banks or from boats, or else pits were dug on the shore in the animals' favorite grazing areas.

In the Bible the hippopotamus is mentioned explicitly only once, in the book of Job. But it may also be referred to elsewhere, in expressions such as "the beasts that dwell among the reeds" (Ps. 68:30) and "the beasts of the Negeb" (Isa. 30:6).

The Horse

A Hebrew poet once compared his beloved to "a mare of Pharaoh's chariots" (Song of Sol. 1:9), thus showing his appreciation for what is probably the most handsome of all the domesticated mammals. Closely related to the donkey, the horse has shorter ears, a longer mane with a forelock, a long, hairy tail, and a soft, sensitive muzzle. The horse's hoof, like that of all ungulates, is actually the enlarged nail of its one remaining toe (originally it had five, but through the ages it lost all but the third, or middle, toe, although small vestiges of the second and fourth remain).

The original home of the horse was on the steppes of Central Asia. In these open expanses the special aptitudes of the horse reached their full development—the horse is an excellent runner and also has a highly developed sense of smell. From the interior of Asia horse breeding spread south and west.

CLASSIFICATION. *Equus caballus* (domestic horse), member of Equidae family of order Perissodactyla (odd-toed hoofed mammals).

LEXICON. Horse—*Hebrew:* SUS. Also, SUSAH (company of horses). *Greek:* HIPPOS. Horseman or rider—*Hebrew:* PARASH. Also, RAKKAB, BAAL. *Greek:* HIPPEUS. Also, HIPPIKON (cavalry).

The oldest Near Eastern records of horses being used to draw chariots come from the Hyksos, a warlike Asiatic people who from 1800-1600 B.C. had conquered the northeastern part of Mesopotamia and the northern part of Syria. The Israelites of patriarchal times seem not to have used horses, for whenever the horse is mentioned in the Pentateuch it is used by the Egyptians or by some other neighbor. The horse probably became common in Egypt during the Eighteenth Dynasty (about 1400 B.C.), for it is pictured in Egyptian art and mention is made of horse-drawn war chariots in the papyri of this period.

APPEARANCE IN BIBLE

This evidence is closely related to what we find in the Bible. No horses were among the gifts that Pharaoh presented to Abraham (Gen. 12:16), but by the time of Joseph they had been introduced in Egypt (Gen. 47:17), not only in the army, but also to draw the chariot in which Joseph, then an Egyptian official of high rank, rode.

After the Exodus the Israelites encountered horses and chariots among the armies of the Canaanites, but still did not adopt them. Horse-drawn chariots were most effective where the terrain was reasonably flat, and much of Canaan was hilly. Deborah witnessed a battle involving war chariots on the Plain of Jezreel, and in her victory chant about the fall of Sisera she sings: "Then loud beat the horses' hoofs with the galloping, galloping of his steeds" (Judg. 5:22). It was the sound of Sisera's nine hundred iron-clad chariots fleeing before Barak. The victory was all the more stirring because the Canaanite war chariots were feared by the Israelites. When Joshua was alloting land to the twelve tribes, the sons of Joseph complained: "All the Canaanites who dwell in the plain have chariots of iron" (Josh. 17:16).

The war chariots of the ancient Near East were two-wheelers and had an armor-covered parapet, but beyond this there was

An Egyptian slave reins up a pair of matched steeds (matched so perfectly in the painting that it is difficult to discern more than one) for his master's one-man battle chariot. The depiction appears in a Theban tomb of the Nineteenth Dynasty. (Photograph courtesy of the Oriental Institute of the University of Chicago.)

considerable variation among the different nations. The parapets could be curved, arched, or angular. The wheels could have four, six, or eight spokes and were sometimes studded with large nails. Most often the war chariot was drawn by two horses, but occasionally four were used in a brace (see the illustration for "The Ass," p. 11). Usually each chariot was manned by a driver and a warrior, but in the Hittite chariots there was a third man, the shield bearer. Occasionally only one person would man a war chariot, in which case he would wrap the reins around his waist to free his hands for battle.

Only after the kingdom had been firmly established did the Israelites take to using horses. Neither Saul nor David had them; they fought on foot, and when they needed quick transportation they used what the patriarchs and judges had used through the centuries—donkeys and camels. Throughout Israelite history horses had been regarded as something alien and even "impious," something which ought not to have any place among the Chosen People. When in the course of war Joshua captured some horses, he simply had them hamstrung, rendering them useless (Josh. 11:9), for he felt that to make use of them as part of the spoils of war would have been against the will of God (Josh. 11:6). David also followed this practice; after he vanquished King Hadadezer of Zobah and captured seventeen hundred riders, he had all but one hundred of their horses hamstrung (II Sam. 8:4). Both Israelite leaders were simply observing the law of God: "When you come into the land which the Lord your God gives you . . . you may indeed set as king over you him whom the Lord your God will choose. . . . Only he must not multiply horses for himself, or cause the people to return to Egypt in order to multiply horses" (Deut. 17:14-16). Apparently anything reminiscent of the hated Egyptians was taboo for those whose history had really begun with the Exodus.

SIGN OF ARROGANCE

Thus, when David's son Absalom "got himself a chariot and horses, and fifty men to run before him" (II Sam. 15:1), he was not only being arrogant, but was toying with apostasy. This quotation introduces the account of Absalom's rebellion, and to an Israelite of the time it clearly expressed the young man's vanity and obstinacy—he wanted to be king, and in a manner different from that of his father. The attitude was not restricted to Absalom among David's ambitious sons; when his father became old, Adonijah also "exalted himself, saying, 'I will be king'; and he prepared for himself chariots and horsemen, and fifty men to run before him" (I Kings 1:5). By now horsemanship seemed to have become a symbol of the new generation's ambitions, and so when Solomon eventually became king, he had none of his father's scruples about using horses in Israel. In an effort to build up a mighty army, he bought horses from Egypt and Cilicia, and at rather inflationary prices: "A chariot could be imported from Egypt for six hundred shekels of silver, and a horse for a hundred and fifty" (I Kings 10:29). With these he introduced charioteer divisions into his army and stationed part of them in Jerusalem and part in the specially prepared garrison towns that had been established or rebuilt by means of indentured labor, Megiddo and Gezer, for example. These became known as the "chariot cities" and "horsemen cities" (I Kings 9:19). According to I Kings 10:26, Solomon at one time had no less than fourteen hundred chariots and twelve thousand horsemen. Recent excavations in Palestine have made it possible to reconstruct the stable facilities in at least one of Solomon's chariot cities, and they show that the fortress of Megiddo could accommodate almost five hundred horses.

RELIED ON EGYPT

In later years it quite often happened that the Israelite armies did not have a sufficient number of horses for their chariots (II Kings 7:13; 18:23). It was important to be on good terms with Egypt, therefore, for its great stud farms of strong and fiery horses were famous. The prophets found much to complain about in this reliance upon another nation's resources; to go to Egypt for help, to "depend on chariots and horses," was often synonymous with materialism and unbelief. Isaiah, for instance, declares: "Woe to those who go down to Egypt for help and rely on horses, who trust in chariots because they are many and in horsemen because they are very strong, but do not look to the Holy One of Israel or consult the Lord!" (Isa. 31:1; see also Ezek. 17:15; Hos. 1:7; 14:3; Mic. 5:10; Zech. 9:10).

The use of cavalry units in Near Eastern warfare was not introduced until the time of the Persians, although individual soldiers—messengers, adjutants, et cetera—rode on horseback before then (see II Kings 9:18, for example). Thus Ezekiel was familiar with the sight of armies of cavalry: "You will

Well-coiffured and "crowned" horses are the tribute that this Mede brings to King Sargon of the Persians in this stone relief found in Sargon II's palace at Dur Sharrukin. (Photograph courtesy of the Metropolitan Museum of Art; gift of John D. Rockefeller, Jr., 1933.)

bestir yourself . . . you and many peoples with you, all of them riding on horses, a great host, a mighty army" (Ezek. 38:14-15).

"LIKE A HORSE . . ."

The authors of the Bible, especially of the later books of the Old Testament, were generally quite familiar with the horse and its characteristics. In his description of Israel's deliverance from Egypt, Isaiah speaks of how the Lord led his people: "Like a horse in the desert, they did not stumble" (Isa. 63:13). The horses in arid regions of the Near East— like Arabian horses today—could move across a desert with swiftness and freedom of movement; Isaiah is expressing the miraculous ease with which the Israelites crossed the Red

Sea. On the other hand, when Jeremiah wanted to confront his people with their unbridled wickedness, he compared them to speeding war horses, known for their recklessness and lust for action regardless of the consequences (Jer. 8:6). The prancing and neighing of stallions in the rutting season are used to characterize the citizens of Jerusalem living their godless and wanton lives (Jer. 5:8; Ezek. 23:20). And the disciplining of a horse by means of bridle and whip is mentioned frequently, usually as a warning (Ps. 32:9; Prov. 26:3; Jas. 3:3).

The use of horseshoes was unknown in biblical times, and hence it was regarded as a special advantage if a horse's hoofs were hard: "Their horses' hoofs seem like flint" (Isa. 5:28). Stirrups were not used, but saddlecloths were common (Ezek. 27:20; Judg. 5:10), as were other accessories: in his description of the coming glory of Jerusalem the prophet envisions that even horse bells shall bear the inscription "Holy to the Lord" (Zech. 14:20). And the "royal crown" on the horse's head in Esther 6:8 must be understood in terms of the luxurious headgear with which the Assyrians, among others, decorated their horses.

BREED NOT KNOWN

We know nothing of the breed of horses that was common in Palestine in biblical times; quite likely they resembled the relatively small but swift animals that appear in Egyptian and Assyrian art. There might be a temptation to think of them as closely related to the magnificent Arabian horses, but this cannot be, for the Arabs took up horse breeding rather late. The prophet Zechariah mentions different colors of horses: red, black, white, and dappled gray (Zech. 6:2-3). In the book of Revelation there is another mention of horses of different colors: white, fiery red, black, and pale yellow; but these are the mounts of the "four horsemen of the Apocalypse," and the colors are more symbolic than descriptive (Rev. 6:1-8).

The Hyrax

In the King James Version of the Bible the Hebrew word *shaphan* was translated "coney," which is usually a name for a member of the rabbit family. But there is general agreement now that the animal intended must have been the hyrax, known also as the rock badger and, in Syria, as the daman. The RSV uses "rock badger" or "badger," but this name too can be misleading, for the true badger belongs to the order Carnivora, while the hyrax belongs to a separate order called Hyracoidea. To complicate matters further, "coney" is still a popular name for this creature (probably because of King James usage). In the interests of zoological accuracy, it is called the hyrax here.

PROVERBIALLY WISE

The hyrax is mentioned three times in the Old Testament. The first time is in the list of unclean animals in the Pentateuch: "Among those that chew the cud or part the hoof, you shall not eat these: . . . and the [hyrax], because it

---

CLASSIFICATION. *Hyrax syriacus,* member of Procaviidae family of order Hyracoidea (one of the ungulate orders).
LEXICON. *Hebrew:* SHAPHAN.

chews the cud but does not part the hoof, is unclean to you"
(Lev. 11:4-5). The next is in praise of God's creative activity:
"The high mountains are for the wild goats; the rocks are a
refuge for the [hyrax]" (Ps. 104:18). Third, it is mentioned
in a proverb that names four things that "on earth are small,
but they are exceedingly wise," the ant, the locust, the lizard,
and the hyrax: "The [hyraxes] are a people not mighty, yet
they make their homes in the rocks" (Prov. 30:24-28).

SUCTION CUP FEET

The hyrax is about the same size as the hare, with a thick
body, rather short legs, and a high, arched back. Its fur is
thick, fine, and soft, gray on the back with occasional long
black hairs, and lighter, almost white, on the belly. It has
four toes on its front feet and three toes on its hind feet, and
almost appears to have hoofs because of its broad, crescent-
shaped nails. It is not, however, classified with the true ungulates. Its toes are connected with skin folds, almost like
webbed feet, and it walks on the soles of its feet, which are
equipped with pads kept moist by numerous glands—as a
result, its feet form natural "suction cups" that are useless
for digging but enable it to climb the steepest and most slip-
pery rock surfaces. The hyrax's tail is so short it can barely
be seen, and its ears are round and small. Its teeth, which
resemble on a small scale those of the hippopotamus, are
adapted for plant food, and when it chews, it moves its jaws
from side to side just like the ruminants.

In Palestine today hyraxes can be found in the rocky area
around the Dead Sea. Their mode of living, like their general
appearance, is similar to that of marmots (relatives of wood-
chucks). They live together in colonies on the mountains and
spend much of the time sunning themselves on the rocks.
Guards are posted, and if approaching danger is sighted, the
whole group will scurry for cover, warned by the guards'
sharp whistles.

This furry creature might easily be mistaken for a rodent of some kind, were it not for its strange feet and its unrodent-like habits. The Old Testament's "coney," its zoological name is the hyrax, and in Syria today it is known as the daman. (Drawing by Carol Wilde.)

The Jackal

The jackal abounds in Asia, Africa, and in the southeastern part of Europe. In ancient times it was also quite common in Palestine and is mentioned several times in the Bible. Although it looks something like the fox, it is a member of the dog genus (*Canis*), and differs from the fox in having a broader skull, a shorter nose, shorter and smaller ears, longer legs, and a shorter tail. The jackal can reach a height of about twenty inches, roughly the size of a German Shepherd. Its back is pale yellow, with dark, almost black, flanks. Its lips are black and its ears are white on the inside.

The similarity between the Palestinian variety of fox and the jackal, in both appearance and living habits, is so great that people in the area do not distinguish between them at times. This confusion found its way into the Bible, where the Hebrew word for fox (*shual*) occasionally appears in a context where the jackal is obviously intended. For example, in contrast to the fox, the jackal prefers to travel in packs, when hunting it attacks openly and with impudence, and in its voraciousness it does not hesitate to eat carrion. Thus when the psalmist uses the Hebrew word for fox in declaring that

---

CLASSIFICATION. *Canis aureus* (common jackal), member of Canidae family (wolves, true dogs, jackals, and foxes) of order Carnivora (flesh-eating mammals).

LEXICON. *Hebrew:* TANNIM, IYYIM, or SHUAL.

---

his enemies "shall be given over to the power of the sword, they shall be prey for foxes" (Ps. 63:10), he actually means a jackal, for a fox rarely will touch corpses, whereas the poet wants to say that his enemies will be carrion.

WITH HYENA

Frequently mentioned in association with the jackal, even though it belongs to yet another genus and is quite different in appearance, is the hyena. The jackal and hyena are mentioned together chiefly because they share two rather distasteful attributes: traveling in rapacious packs, and feeding on carrion. The RSV translates the Hebrew *iyyim* as "hyenas," but there is some doubt that this is a zoologically correct rendering. The King James translators, unfamiliar with either the jackal or the hyena, render *tannim* as "dragons" or "whales" and *iyyim* as "wild beasts of the islands."

"HOWLERS"

One Hebrew word probably used to denote jackals, *iyyim*, literally means "howlers," obviously in reference to the singular noise this animal emits, generally at night. The howl of the jackal sounds like the crying of a child or the heart-rending wail of the bereaved. To other jackals, however, it is merely an invitation, a means of calling the pack together for its nocturnal hunting foray. There is one more Hebrew word for the jackal, *tan*, literally "lengthy," which takes note of the animal's long, slender silhouette.

The jackal's mournful howl became a symbol of pain and lamentation for some biblical authors. For example, Micah expresses his sorrow over the Lord's punishment: "I will make lamentation like the jackals" (Mic. 1:8). And Job makes clear the intensity of his pain by calling himself "a brother of jackals" (Job 30:29).

The jackal lives in desolate places: in caves, ravines, rocky deserts, and abandoned ruins. The jackal was so closely asso-

To the Israelites the jackal symbolized desolation, but to their former captors the Egyptians it represented one of the forms taken by the god Anubis. Here Anubis perches majestically on a funerary chest from the tomb of Tutenkhamon. (Photograph by Harry Burton; the Metropolitan Museum of Art.)

ciated with the desert that the phrase "place of jackals" was commonly used instead of the word "desert" (for example, Ps. 44:19). When Isaiah proclaims the Lord's punishment upon the nation of Edom and describes how the present stronghold shall become overgrown with thorns, he declares: "It shall be the haunt of jackals" (Isa. 34:13). Similarly he describes the fall of Babylon: "Hyenas will cry in its towers, and jackals in the pleasant palaces" (Isa. 13:22). In Jeremiah's depictions of destruction, too, the symbol of the jackal creates a cold and sinister mood: "Therefore wild beasts and jackals shall dwell in Babylon" (Jer. 50:39); "I will make Jerusalem a heap of ruins, a lair of jackals" (Jer. 9:11; cf. Jer. 10:22; 49:33; 51:37).

The Leopard

One of the larger cats and one of the most dangerous of all predatory animals, the leopard is somewhat smaller than a tiger, its body measuring up to five feet in length with a tail of about thirty inches. But its body is better proportioned than the tiger's—it is sleek, powerful, and muscular, and its

---

CLASSIFICATION. *Felis pardus,* member of Felidae family (cats) of order Carnivora (flesh-eating mammals).
LEXICON. *Hebrew:* NAMER, NEMAR. *Greek:* PARDALIS.

---

movements are unusually lithe and graceful. The leopard has a golden coat that becomes almost white on the belly, with the back and sides covered with black markings or spots that are grouped in various patterns. What seems to be merely random decoration, however, enables the animal to conceal itself in the flickering patterns of light and shadow in the jungle.

PROBABLY COMMON

The leopard is mentioned on occasion in the Old Testament, and there is much to suggest that it may have been fairly common in the Palestine of biblical times. For one thing, a few leopards are still to be encountered there; for another, several place names that appear in the Bible would seem to have been derived from the Hebrew name for the leopard (namer), undoubtedly because there were areas nearby that were much-frequented haunts of these universally feared beasts of prey.

Beth-nimrah, that is, "the home of the leopard," was allotted to the sons of Gad, who built a city there, on the far side of the Jordan but not far from its banks (Num. 32:3, 36; Josh. 13:27). "The waters of Nimrim," mentioned by both Isaiah (15:6) and Jeremiah (48:34), was a fertile spot southeast of the Dead Sea; leopards are still found there. In the Song of Solomon appears a reference to "the mountains of leopards" (Song of Sol. 4:8), but it is not clear whether this is meant to be a place name or simply a poetic description.

A SILENT AMBUSH

The hunting technique of the leopard—like that of some other large cats—involves taking the victim by surprise from a silent ambush. The leopard conceals itself near villages or watering places and waits for its prey, often remaining in one spot for long spans of time; only the occasional whisking motion of its tail betrays the silent animal's intense excitement and alertness. Superior even to the lion and the tiger in suppleness and agility, though not as strong, the leopard can approach its prey without a sound and then pounce upon it with one mighty, death-dealing leap.

Birds, antelopes, monkeys, jackals, and many other hapless creatures fall victim to it, and its bloodthirstiness is sometimes rather gruesome. There is a case on record of a leopard that gained entrance to a goat pen and killed all thirty-nine goats within it, eating what it could and letting the rest lie. Biblical authors, among them Jeremiah, were keenly aware of the leopard's lethal manner of hunting. "A leopard is watching against their cities," says Jeremiah (5:6), presenting a sinister picture of the doom that awaits his people as punishment for their unfaithfulness—and his hearers knew the horror of such a fate. Hosea too describes the wrath of God against his Chosen People, who had forgotten him, as a leopard lurking by the wayside (Hos. 13:7).

IT SHALL LIE DOWN . . .

Thus the leopard is justly feared; in addition, it is a difficult animal to track down, for it can climb, jump, and swim with great skill, it follows no set pattern of behavior, and it is far less dependent on drinking water than most other beasts of prey. Isaiah, then, could hardly have chosen a more striking illustration of the glory of the future kingdom of peace than his familiar saying that "the leopard shall lie down with the kid" (Isa. 11:6).

"Can the Ethiopian change his skin or the leopard his spots? Then also you can do good who are accustomed to do evil" (Jer. 13:23). The plaintive sigh of the prophet has passed into common speech as a way of expressing a person's intransigence. It is an apt image, for most human beings "accustomed to do evil" seem as capable of doing good as the leopard is capable of changing the pattern of its coat—or, for that matter, its ferocious and untamable nature.

The Lion

The well-known "king of the beasts," recognized in the Bible by its "stately tread" and by its courage, for it "does not turn back before any" (Prov. 30:29), is the largest and most powerful of the cats. The Persian lion, a subspecies native to the Near East and one of the smallest breeds, is about five feet long with a tasseled tail about thirty inches long, and has strong, muscular foreparts; its shoulders reach a height of between thirty and thirty-five inches. Other breeds, such as the Barbary, Atlas, and Masai lions, are considerably larger, up to eight feet long with a three-foot tail. All have tawny coats with no markings and a regal appearance, which is emphasized in the Atlas and Masai varieties by large, almost black manes that cover the neck and shoulders of the male.

The lioness has a gestation period of about a hundred and ten days, after which it gives birth to a litter of from two to

---

CLASSIFICATION. *Felis leo,* member of Felidae family (cats) of order Carnivora (flesh-eating mammals).

LEXICON. *Hebrew:* ARI, ARYEH. Also, LABI, LEBAIM, LAYISH, or SHACHAL; LEBIYAH (lioness); KEPHIR (young lion); SHACHATS (pride). *Greek:* LEON.

six cubs. At seven years of age the lion is in its prime, weighing from four to almost six hundred pounds, depending on the breed. Lions in captivity have been known to reach the age of seventy years, but the more normal life span is thirty.

Wild lions are usually encountered in pairs but occasionally also in small groups, or "prides." They hunt mainly during the night and sleep during the day in lairs that are used for only a few days at a time and are usually only natural hollows in the ground. The lion attacks its victims from ambush, lying in wait in the tall grass near water holes to catch all kinds of herbivores, such as deer, antelope, gazelles, and zebras. It kills smaller animals with a single blow of its paw; larger animals, such as buffalo and oxen, it dispatches by tearing at the throat with its teeth.

FREQUENT IN ANTIQUITY

At the present time no lions exist in Palestine, though they are still encountered in Arabia and in regions near the Tigris and Euphrates rivers. In antiquity the lion was much more common throughout the Near East than it is today, and from the many passages in the Bible that mention it, the inference can be drawn that it was a frequently seen and much feared beast of prey to the Israelites. It is also quite probable that the animal they knew was the Persian lion.

"Behold, like a lion coming up from the jungle of the Jordan against a strong sheepfold, I will suddenly make them run away from her" (Jer. 49:19). Speaking a judgment on Edom, the prophet provides a picture familiar to everyone who had traveled along the river that formed the eastern border of Palestine. Both banks of the Jordan are wooded, almost tropical. Towering above are the crowns of tamarisk trees, terebinths, poplars, and willows, supporting an abundance of bird life; along the ground is an undergrowth with thousands of varieties of grasses, shrubs, and flowers, providing the kind of cover in which both game and predatory animals flourish.

In biblical times lions would come out of thickets to wait along the river's edge for their victim, coming to slake its thirst. "Hark, the wail of shepherds, for their glory is despoiled! Hark, the roar of the lions, for the jungle of the Jordan is laid waste!" (Zech. 11:3). Today the jungle remains, but the roar of the lion is gone.

OTHER HAUNTS

The lion had other haunts as well. It undoubtedly roamed the hilly areas of Judah, although there is no specific reference to this fact. Some biblical passages are explicit in locating the lion's haunts, however: "Come with me from Lebanon, my bride. . . . Depart from the peak of Amana, from the peak of Senir and Hermon, from the dens of lions, from the mountains of leopards" (Song of Sol. 4:8). The mountain kingdom of Lebanon lay north of Palestine proper, and some of its peaks, snow-capped Mount Hermon among them, are nine thousand feet high. Along the slopes and valleys grew prodigious forests of cedar and cypress, sheltering myriads of wild animals; and those that shunned forest life found asylum in the many deep ravines and caves of the mountains. The Negeb, a Judean wilderness stretching south toward the borders of Egypt, also provided habitation for lions: "An oracle on the beasts of the Negeb. Through a land of trouble and anguish, from where come the lioness and the lion . . ." (Isa. 30:6).

DAVID AND THE LIONS

Biblical personages were often thrown into conflict with the mightiest predator of all. The shepherd boy David had to contend not only with bears (q.v.), but also with lions intent on feasting upon his father's flock. It was a dangerous life, but it developed the resourcefulness, courage, and strength that he needed later, both as national hero and as king. "Your servant has killed . . . lions . . ." he told Saul before going out to battle Goliath (I Sam. 17:36). Samson, an earlier

Israelite hero, was also on intimate terms with lions—one he tore asunder with his bare hands, "as one tears a kid" (Judg. 14:6). By no means was the lion always the loser in this combat in the biblical accounts. There is the narration of a lion attacking and killing "the man of God who came from Judah," an event afterward interpreted by an old prophet of Bethel to be a just punishment from the Lord, for "the man of God" had disobeyed the word of the Lord (I Kings 13:20-27; cf. I Kings 20:36, where another prophet's disobedience to the Lord's command is similarly rewarded). After the king of Assyria had caused Samaria to become depopulated and then permitted foreign colonists to settle only in its cities, roving bands of lions began attacking the newcomers, who "did not fear the Lord" (II Kings 17:24-25).

The lion, contrary to what most jungle movies would have us believe, does not automatically attack humans. Generally it attacks only out of great hunger or in self-defense. But there are two periods in its life when it is especially apt to attack people without undue provocation: when it is young (from eighteen to thirty months) it can become very dangerous if it develops a taste for human flesh; and when, at an advanced age, it has been expelled from its band for no longer being fast enough to keep up with the pursuit of swift animals like antelopes and gazelles.

SAMSON'S RIDDLE

Biblical authors, as was almost always the case, were quite observant of the characteristics of the lion. A knowledge of the animal's strength is an important clue to Samson's riddle: "What is sweeter than honey? What is stronger than a lion?" (Judg. 14:18). It seemed impossible that any creature could have more strength; in fact, one of the Hebrew names for the lion, *layish*, is derived directly from a root that means "to be strong." Hezekiah's memoirs show an awareness of the lion's potency; in his description of the ferocity of the

Stately in its tread, mightiest among beasts, declares the proverb, and King Nebuchadnezzar II of Babylon evidently agreed when he had the famous Procession Street built in the sixth century B.C. (Photograph courtesy of the Metropolitan Museum of Art; Fletcher Fund, 1931.)

illness that brought him close to death he wrote: "Like the lion he breaks all my bones" (Isa. 38:13).

The usual hunting time for the lion is at dusk, and before it sets out it utters three or four resonant roars that are further amplified by the way the lion holds its head to the ground; thus the psalmist knows what it means when "young lions roar for their prey" (Ps. 104:21). It was a sound to inspire fear, as the prophets attest: "They shall roar together like lions; they shall growl like lions' whelps" (Jer. 51:38; cf. Isa. 5:29). Another psalmist recognizes the relative helplessness of the lion without its fangs: referring to the wicked, he pleads: "Tear out the fangs of the young lions, O Lord!" (Ps. 58:6). And Ezekiel well knew how dangerous was the young lion once it had tasted human flesh; of the last king of Israel he says: "He became a young lion, and he learned to catch prey; he devoured men" (Ezek. 19:3).

THE FIGURATIVE LION

Many of the biblical references to the lion are used in a figurative sense, not only in allegories such as are found in Ezekiel, but also as symbols of the spiritual qualities of men. Quite naturally "lion" came to be used as a name for good men of courage and strength (a practice that has been carried through the ages: for example, Richard the Lionhearted). Thus, in Jacob's blessing is said: "Judah is a lion's whelp: from the prey, my son, you have gone up. He stooped down, he crouched as a lion, and as a lioness; who dares rouse him up?" (Gen. 49:9). The book of Proverbs declares: "The righteous are bold as a lion" (Prov. 28:1), implying that an upright man need fear nothing. The lion's proud, majestic appearance was used figuratively to express the frightening aspect of the warrior. Some of the earlier followers of David are described as men "whose faces were like the faces of lions" (I Chron. 12:8). In contrast, the lion could be used to emphasize the cruelty and wickedness of an enemy. A psalmist dramatically describes the dangerous nature of the godless as equal to that of an attacking lion: "He lurks in secret like a lion in his covert; he lurks that he may seize the poor, he seizes the poor when he draws him into his net" (Ps. 10:9). The greatest enemy of all, the devil himself, is compared to a "roaring lion, seeking some one to devour" (I Pet. 5:8). All the more impressive, then, is the prophet's picture: "The lion shall eat straw like the ox" (Isa. 11:7).

The image of the lion is also used for God, who in his righteous anger will not be deterred by any obstacles: "As a lion or a young lion growls over his prey, and when a band of shepherds is called forth against him is not terrified by their shouting or daunted at their noise, so the Lord of hosts

will come down to fight upon Mount Zion and upon its hill"
(Isa. 31:4; cf. Hos. 5:14).

The Old Testament mentions the lion more than any other
wild animal, about one hundred and thirty times. In the less
rugged civilization of New Testament times, the references
are much scarcer, partly because the animals were nowhere
near so numerous as formerly. But the highly poetic language of the book of Revelation employs the lion as a symbol
of Christ, the unvanquished hero who in his fight for the sal-

A hapless bullock falls prey to this Persian lion on the stairway
of Apadana at Persepolis, the fortress city of ancient Persia.
The sculptor has conveyed a magnificent feeling of the lion's
great strength and ferocity. (Photograph courtesy of the Oriental
Institute of the University of Chicago.)

vation of the faithful destroys the kingdom of Satan. In a statement that harks back to the prophecy in Gen. 49:9 we are told: "Lo, the Lion of the tribe of Judah, the Root of David, has conquered" (Rev. 5:5).

A pair of glum lions, with definite expressions of disappointment on their faces, watch Daniel offer a prayer of thanksgiving to the Lord in this ivory diptych panel of Daniel 6 from fourteenth-century England. (Photograph courtesy of the Metropolitan Museum of Art; gift of J. Pierpont Morgan, 1917.)

The Mole Rat

"In that day men will cast forth their idols of silver and their idols of gold, which they made for themselves to worship, to the moles and to the bats," declares Isaiah in his dramatic description of the Day of the Lord, that day when the Lord shall turn against "all that is proud and lofty" and when "the pride of men shall be brought low" (Isa. 2:20, 12, 17).

Found only in this particular passage, the Hebrew word *chapharperah*, translated as "moles" in our Bibles, means literally "a burrowing animal," and since there are mountain crevices and ravines in the context of the passage, almost any burrowing animal could have been meant. It is highly improbable, however, that the common mole (*Talpa europaea*) is meant here, for this creature does not (and most likely did not) inhabit Palestine. Besides, the common mole is hardly offensive enough to provide fit company for the idols so despised by Isaiah and his Lord.

The animal most likely meant is the mole rat, a rodent about eight inches long. Hidden in the fur of the rather thickset head with its blunt nose are the ears and the almost sightless eyes, which are no larger than poppy seeds. Its teeth are

---

CLASSIFICATION. *Spalax typhlus,* member of Spalacidae family of order Rodentia (rodents).

LEXICON. *Hebrew:* CHAPHARPERAH.

Although unrelated to the mole, the mole rat shares
many of that animal's features and habits. But the
ratlike tail reveals that it is indeed a rodent. (Drawing by Carol Wilde.)

typical of rodents', strong and protruding like those of the
squirrel. The neck is short and thick, the body plump and
shaped like a sausage. The short legs have broad paws, with
strong claws for burrowing. The fur is soft, thick, and ashen
gray. Although unrelated to the common mole (which is in a
different order, the insectivores), the mole rat has similar
habits. It digs itself deep and roomy tunnels, preferably in
dry, sandy, stony soil or in loose gravel. Appearing above
the ground occasionally at night, it feeds primarily on vege-
tables, roots, and bulbs, and can do much harm to gardens.

The mole rat is found in southern Europe, western Asia,
and—in large numbers—in the vicinity of Jerusalem. Undoubtedly it was considered just as much of a pest in biblical times
as it is today, and is as ugly a burrowing animal as Isaiah
could have wished to give force to his vision of the downfall
of idolatry.

The Mule

Produced by crossing a male donkey with a female horse, the mule has the body of a horse and the head and tail of an ass. At one time the mule was indispensable on American and European farms, and in the warm latitudes it is still a very useful domestic animal, combining the best traits of both its parents. It has the frugality, endurance, and quiet, steady gait of an ass along with the strength, swiftness, and courage of a horse. The mule is hardy; it readily endures heat, hunger, and thirst. And it is almost never sick; the saying is that a mule becomes sick only when it is ready to die. It lives considerably longer than a horse, but is unable to reproduce itself.

The hardy creature shows its mettle in mountainous regions, where it can carry a load of up to three hundred pounds as far as thirty miles a day. No wonder, then, that the Bible often associates it with the camel as an invaluable pack animal, for the terrain in Palestine is quite rugged in parts. Isaiah's picture of the people of Israel gathering again in Jerusalem from the far corners of the earth after their dispersal gives the mule a place equal to the horse and camel as a means

CLASSIFICATION. Cross of *Equus asinus* (ass) and *Equus caballus* (horse), members of Equidae family of order Perissodactyla (odd-toed hoofed mammals).
LEXICON. *Hebrew:* PERED. Also, PIRDAH.

of transportation: "And they shall bring all your brethren from all the nations as an offering to the Lord, upon horses, and in chariots, and in litters, and upon mules, and upon dromedaries, to my holy mountain Jerusalem, says the Lord" (Isa. 66:20; cf. II Kings 5:17; I Chron. 12:40; Zech. 14:15).

MOUNT FOR A KING

During one stage in Israel's history the mule was the proper mount for a king, and David himself rode upon a mule (I Kings 1:33), as did the offspring of royalty (II Sam. 13:29). Like the horse, but in contrast to the ass, at the time of the kingdom and later the mule was used primarily in battle. Even Absalom, who arrogantly took up the rather profane practice of riding in a horse-drawn chariot, nevertheless used a mule in his armed rebellion against his father. In fact, he met his gruesome end while fleeing by mule (II Sam. 18:9).

IMPORTED MULES

The mule is not mentioned in the Bible before the time of David; but from that time on it is referred to frequently up through the return of the exiles from Babylonia. The exiles brought back with them, among other things, two hundred and forty-five mules (Ezra 2:66; Neh. 7:68). Strangely enough, however, the Israelites were restricted by the law of Moses from breeding their own mules (Lev. 19:19), and they were obliged to import them from abroad. In antiquity Asia Minor was especially noted for breeding fine mules; they were even brought to the city of Tyre from far-off Armenia, if this is the proper meaning for the "Beth-togarmah" mentioned in Ezek. 27:14. Mules are prominent among the gifts of homage which King Solomon received: "And the whole earth sought the presence of Solomon to hear his wisdom, which God had put into his mind. Every one of them brought his present, articles of silver and gold . . . horses, and mules, so much year by year" (I Kings 10:24-25; II Chron. 9:23-24).

The Ox

One of the earliest animals to be domesticated by man (*ca.* 4,000 B.C.) and one of the most valuable throughout history is the ox, a large, cud-chewing beast with a muscular, heavy-set body, relatively short legs and neck, "cloven" hoofs, and a massive forehead that supports its hollow horns. Generally we tend to think of the ox as an ungainly and even comical animal, but often in the Bible its beauty is emphasized. In the blessing of Moses upon Israel, for instance, we read that the "bull has majesty" (Deut. 33:17). Jeremiah compares Egypt to "a beautiful heifer" (Jer. 46:20), and Hosea writes that Ephraim was "a trained heifer that loved to thresh, and I spared her fair neck" (Hos. 10:11). We may infer that the ox these writers knew was indeed an attractive and stately animal, quite different from that native to Palestine in later times.

This view is supported by ancient Egyptian and Babylonian

CLASSIFICATION. *Bos indicus* (zebu), member of Bovidae family of order Artiodactyla (even-toed hoofed mammals).

LEXICON. *Hebrew:* BAQAR. Also, ELEPH (oxen); PAR, PARAH, or EGEL (calf); SHOR or TOR (bull); EGLAH (heifer); BEHEMAH or BEIR (beast); EDER (herd); MIQNEH (possession). *Greek:* BOUS. Also, MOSCHOS (calf); TAUROS (bull); DAMALIS (heifer); AGELE (herd).

---

representations of the ox, which make it clear that the variety of ox found in Palestine in Old Testament times was very closely related to the animal known today as the zebu or East Indian ox. Adherents of the Hindu religion regard the zebu as sacred and will not touch its flesh, and it is certainly a more noble-looking beast than most of the Western breeds, with an arched hump setting off its massive shoulders and emphasizing its great weight, and a calm dignity that is accented by short, straight horns.

EARLIEST OX

The earliest mention of the ox in the Bible occurs, as in the case of the ass, in the story of the valuable gifts that the ruler of Egypt gave to Abraham (Gen. 12:16). That Abraham then brought them to Canaan may have been the narrator's way of suggesting that domesticated cattle existed in Egypt before they did in Canaan, and were imported into the "land of milk and honey" at the time of the patriarchs. There are later references to the large herds of cattle belonging to Abraham (Gen. 18:7; 21:27), which make it seem likely that nomads of the time were able to raise cattle, and not just farmers who were rooted in one spot. Settled farmers were to be found chiefly in Egypt, and the dream of Pharaoh (Gen. 41:1-7) indicates that Egypt was rich in cattle, which grazed in the fields of grass along the banks of the Nile. The Nile delta, and especially the district of Goshen in the northeastern corner of Egypt, were exceptionally well suited for cattle-raising, and Joseph, as a high-ranking Egyptian official, was able to procure this land for his brothers, so that they could thrive as farmers. When Moses was dueling Pharaoh to obtain the release of the people of Israel, he insisted that they be allowed to take their herds along, ostensibly for the purpose of making religious sacrifices (Exod. 10:24-26), but more likely because by this time they had come to depend heavily on cattle for a livelihood and would need them.

In Palestine cattle were nurtured in such choice grazing lands as the Valley of Sharon (I Chron. 27:29), Gilead (Num. 32:1), and the area of Bashan, lying to the east of the Sea of Galilee. The "strong bulls of Bashan" are mentioned in several Bible passages (for example, Ps. 22:12) and they came to provide a poetic image of strong and dangerous enemies for the prophets, while Bashan cows represented luxury-loving women. Amos, the prophet who came out of the rural districts to pronounce the will of the Lord, often used illustrations from husbandry to drive home a point. Even though he was a shepherd from Tekoa, he was familiar enough with the cows of Bashan to know that their owners pampered them like spoiled wives; condemning rich women, Amos said: "Hear this word, you cows of Bashan . . . who say to their husbands, 'Bring, that we may drink!'" (Amos 4:1; cf. Jer. 50:19).

ISAIAH, JOEL, AND JESUS

In any case, cattle, like all domesticated creatures, came to know and depend on their masters, a fact which Isaiah compares ruefully with the obstinate blindness of his people: "The ox knows its owner . . . but Israel does not know, my people does not understand" (Isa. 1:3). There were often times in the Near East when grazing land was threatened by drought (the "lean years" of Pharaoh's dream) or other ravages of nature; Joel gives a pathetic description of the anxiety of the oxen when a swarm of locusts threatens to destroy their food supply: "How the beasts groan! The herds of cattle are perplexed because there is no pasture for them . . ." (Joel 1:18). Joel is probably describing here an invasion of locusts (q.v.) which he had seen himself.

When the cattle returned from pasture they were kept in stalls, some of which were constructed by royal decree, as in the case of King Hezekiah (II Chron. 32:28). There they were fed and watered every day, even on the Sabbath when all other work was forbidden. When Jesus was criticized for healing a woman on the Sabbath, he replied: "Does not each of you on the sabbath untie his ox or his ass from the manger, and lead it away to water it?" (Luke 13:15).

THE FATTED CALF

Oxen have always been a valuable source of meat, and in biblical times the fatted calf, served roasted or boiled, was gourmet fare, suitable for the finest banquet. When Abraham received an unexpected visit from the three impressive strangers, he "ran to the herd, and took a calf, tender and good, and gave it to the servant, who hastened to prepare it" (Gen. 18:7). The father of the prodigal son provided a very famous "fatted calf" for his son's return (Luke 15:23), and the king in Christ's parable who gave a wedding feast for his son sent this message to those who were invited: "My fat calves are killed, and everything is ready" (Matt. 22:4).

Part of a herd was often set aside and fattened in the stalls, so that they would not be able to run off their succulence in the fields. When Amos wanted to show how luxuriously and carelessly the Israelites were living, he declared: "Woe to those who lie upon beds of ivory, and stretch themselves upon their couches, and eat . . . calves from the midst of the stall" (Amos 6:4). And the witch of Endor actually kept a fettered calf within her house, which she killed and served to Saul and his men (I Sam. 28:24-25).

Oxen were also fattened to be sacrificed, as shown in Ezekiel's description of the great sacrificial feast (Ezek. 39:17-20), for they were indispensable to this kind of religious ceremony. Cattle could be brought for sacrifice after they were seven days old (Exod. 22:30; Lev. 22:27).

DRAFT ANIMALS

Finally, the ox was used extensively as a draft animal in Israel, and still is in many parts of the Near East and India. Bulls were preferred for such work, and for this reason many more were kept in a herd than were needed for breeding purposes (one bull for every thirty cows). This explains why Jacob, upon returning home from his service with Laban, gave his brother Esau ten bulls along with forty cows (Gen. 32:15). Before he became a prophet, Elisha plowed his father's fields with "twelve yoke of oxen," that is, twelve pair (I Kings 19:19), which was probably not the complete work force, for the practice was to hold half of the animals in reserve while the rest worked. Before his ordeal Job owned five hundred yoke of oxen, and ultimately he had a thousand; apparently he owned farming land of considerable acreage. Heifers were occasionally put to work plowing, as indicated in Samson's bitter rejoinder to the Philistines: "If you had not plowed with my heifer, you would not have found out my riddle" (Judg. 14:18).

For moving especially heavy objects cows were favored over bulls because of their more docile nature, and thus they were used to transport the ark of the covenant to the land of Israel. When David recovered the ark after it had been lost for many years, this precaution was neglected; as a result, the oxen drawing the ark stumbled, and a man named Uzzah put out his hand to prevent it from toppling over and was struck dead on the spot for profaning the holy object (II Sam. 6:6-7). The ox was also used as a pack animal (I Chron. 12:40), although it did not have the endurance possessed by the ass, camel, or mule.

THRESHERS

Oxen were used for various other tasks, including threshing. The restriction in the Pentateuch not to "muzzle an ox when it treads out the grain" (Deut. 25:4) is actually a humane piece of legislation. Threshing with cattle involved simply turning the animals loose in the threshing field where the sheaves lay, whereupon they would eventually trample the kernels of grain out of the sheaves. To deny the working ani-

The flowing beard of this Sumerian ox is probably not intended to be realistic, but supports the impression that ancient Near Easterners considered the ox a majestic, handsome creature. This copper head dates from the third millennium B.C. (Photograph courtesy of the Metropolitan Museum of Art; Fletcher Fund, 1947.)

mals the opportunity to eat the grain that lay beneath them was considered a senseless cruelty.

In the Near East the buying of a yoke of oxen is an event of major importance; the first thing one does after the purchase is to test the animals in the field to find out how much the dealer has exaggerated their worth. When business is to be done, the Oriental does not spare his superlatives, and the buyer cannot be too careful. In his parable of the great wedding feast, Jesus has one of the invited guests give this excuse: "I have bought five yoke of oxen, and I go to examine them; I pray you, have me excused" (Luke 14:19). This reason was a more serious matter than it may seem to us today; Jesus was pointing out that even the best excuses are superseded by the Master's invitation. Once in possession of oxen, a person required only one piece of essential equipment with which to control them, a stick or oxgoad. This goad could be a formidable weapon as well, for Shamgar is said to have

slaughtered six hundred Philistines with one (Judg. 3:31). Paul apparently was aware of its other uses, for in his narration of his conversion, he recalls the voice of Jesus saying to him: "It hurts you to kick against the goads" (Acts 26:14).

MILK, A FAVORITE DRINK

One final benefit provided by the multi-purpose cow deserves mention—its milk was as much a boon to the Israelites as it is to us today. It was a favorite drink among the patriarchs, for Abraham offered it to his honored guests (Gen. 18:8), and Jael gave Sisera milk as refreshment (Judg. 4:19). Canaan was described to the wandering people of Israel as a land "flowing with milk and honey" (Exod. 3:8), which meant that it was almost an earthly paradise. The prophecy of Joel that "the hills shall flow with milk" (Joel 3:18) has the same connotation.

Milk had several highly prized by-products, among them the curd that is mentioned so often in the Old Testament, which was probably something like cottage cheese. Abraham offered his guests curds and milk with their fatted calf, and when, thirsty and exhausted, David and his followers came to Mahanaim, the inhabitants brought them honey and curds (II Sam. 17:29; cf. Isa. 7:15). Cheese is also mentioned in the Bible; the book of Job uses the process of curdling milk to make cheese in a rather strange comparison with the way a child is formed in its mother's womb: "Remember that thou hast made me of clay," Job says to the Lord, "and wilt thou turn me to dust again? Didst thou not pour me out like milk and curdle me like cheese?" (Job 10:9-10).

Persian depictions of the ox, dating from the sixth century B.C., support the view that the oxen known to biblical writers resembled the zebu. Note the pronounced hump above the animal's shoulders. Here a bull is part of a tribute being offered to a king, as carved on the walls of Persepolis. (Photograph courtesy of the Oriental Institute of the University of Chicago.)

The Sea Cow

Forming a small, special order of mammals by itself, the sea cow resembles the whale in certain respects, and the elephant in others, without being related to either. A rather clumsily built, sluggish animal that lives in salt water, it varies in length from nine to fifteen feet, and has a bulky, spindle-shaped body resembling that of a large fish. The relatively small head is set on an almost imperceptible neck, and, with its thick lips, it somewhat resembles the head of the hippopotamus; its molars, from five to eleven in number, are cusp-shaped, and in place of incisors it has sharp, horny growths with which it bites. Its eyes and ears are quite small, and its nostrils are located on the upper side of the nose so that it can breathe without exposing its body above the water's surface, and thus it is able to conceal itself in much the same way that the hippopotamus hides itself.

The front limbs, which are located just behind the ears,

CLASSIFICATION. *Dugong dugong*, member of Dugongidae family of order Sirenia (sea cows).

LEXICON. *Hebrew:* TACHASH.

---

resemble flippers because of their webbed toes. As in the elephant, the female's mammary glands are located one under each armpit. The sea cow has no hind limbs, but its tail has developed into a strong horizontal fin that is crescent-shaped and flat. The smooth skin is leaden gray with a bluish tinge, marked here and there with longitudinal stripes of darker gray and sparsely covered with fine hairs that are as stiff as bristles. The hide is very tough and is used in some localities, including areas along the coastline of the Mediterranean Sea, for handmade sandals.

HUNTED TO EXTINCTION

The sea cow has a preference for brackish water near the shore. Its favorite haunts are lagoons and estuaries. It seldom ventures onto land, and it can be submerged for four minutes or longer without coming up for air; lying on the bottom of the sea, it feeds on marine vegetation. Sea cows are often found in pairs, but seldom in larger groups. Because they are anything but alert creatures they are quite easily hunted—in some areas to the point of extermination—both for their hides and their flesh. Arabs are among those who consider sea cow meat a delicacy, but its rather sweet taste repels many people accustomed to less exotic fare. There are only a few species of sea cow in the oceans of the world, one of which, called the dugong, is found in the Red Sea and along the coasts of the Indian Ocean.

THE MYSTERIOUS "TACHASH"

This strange creature is included here because a consensus of present-day interpreters of the Bible who have troubled themselves with the question believe that it is the mysterious animal called *tachash* in the Old Testament. One mention is in Exodus, where various directions are being given the Israelites concerning voluntary contributions toward the building of the tabernacle: "The Lord said to Moses, 'Speak to the people of Israel, that they take for me an offering . . . gold, silver, and bronze, blue and purple and scarlet stuff and fine twined linen, goats' hair, tanned rams' skins, [tachash] skins . . ." (Exod. 25:1-5).

GOATS AND BADGERS

The RSV translates tachash here as "goat," without a great deal of basis except that it fits the context, while the King James translators were a bit more adventurous and used the phrase "badgers' skins." However, the only "badger" to be found in the area was the rock badger or hyrax (q.v.), whose pelts would be out of place among the rich accoutrements of the tabernacle. But the skin of the sea cow can be tanned into a handsome leather.

The other reference to tachash, in Ezekiel, shows that it was also used as shoe leather (as it still is today): "I clothed you also with embroidered cloth and shod you with [tachash], I swathed you in fine linen and covered you with silk" (Ezek. 16:10). With these words the prophet contrasts his people's sinfulness with the rich bounty they have received, and once again the tachash skin (again called "badgers' skin" by the KJV, but simply "leather" by the RSV) is among luxurious company.

"BLUE LEATHER"

To further support the thesis that the animal whose hide is in question here is the sea cow, the Septuagint, a first century B.C. translation of the Old Testament into Greek, translates the two phrases as "blue leather" and "blue footwear," apparently with reference to the bluish tinge of the sea cow's hide. Finally, the word used for the sea cow in present-day Arabic is tuchash, an obvious cognate of the Hebrew word. The accumulation of evidence would seem sufficient to justify placing the sea cow in a biblical bestiary and thus solving the mystery of the tachash.

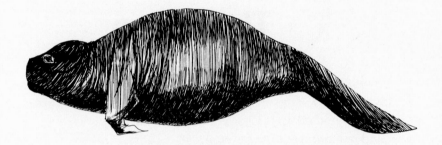

Certainly not to be included among the handsomest creatures of the animal kingdom, the sea cow is nevertheless harmless, and lives a quiet, sedentary life—much like that of the land animal for which it is named. (Drawing by Carol Wilde.)

95

The Sheep

Rather closely related to the goat, both biologically and in popular thinking, the sheep is differentiated by its lower forehead, its angulated spiral horns marked with transverse wrinkles and curved slightly outward, its covering of wool (in domesticated breeds), and its lack of a "goatee." The ox, the goat, and the sheep are all members of the same family (Bovidae) and thus share the following characteristics: "cloven" hoofs, hollow horns, and the third stomach of the cud-chewer.

There are many species of wild sheep and dozens of breeds of the common domesticated sheep, but probably the sheep found in Palestine during biblical times was the species known as the "fat-tailed sheep." Unlike its relatives, this variety has a long, broad, fat-filled tail that by itself weighs from ten to fifteen pounds on the mature animal—and on some rams as much as thirty pounds. In the Mosaic law these sheep are

---

CLASSIFICATION. *Ovis laticaudata* (fat-tailed sheep), member of Bovidae family in Pecora group (true ruminants) of order Artiodactyla (even-toed hoofed mammals).

LEXICON. *Hebrew:* TSON, TSONEH. Also, EDER or MARITH (flock); AYIL, DEKAR (ram); RACHEL (ewe); KEBES, KESEB, SEH, IMMERIN, or TELAIM (lambs); TALEH, KAR (he-lamb); KABSAH (she-lamb); ZEMER (mountain-sheep). *Greek:* PROBATON. Also, AMNOS, ARNION (lamb); POIMNE, POIMNION (flock).

mentioned repeatedly in the regulations regarding the manner in which sacrifices should be presented: "If he offers a lamb for his offering, then he shall offer it before the Lord. . . . Then from the sacrifice of the peace offering by fire to the Lord he shall offer its fat, the fat tail entire . . ." (Lev. 3:7, 9; cf. Exod. 29:22; Lev. 7:3; 8:25; 9:19). The creature's substantial tail was much favored for sacrifice; it was used in the peace offering, the sin offering, and the guilt offering.

THE RAM'S HORN

Only the ram of the fat-tailed variety has horns. From two to three inches in diameter, they can be potent weapons. The Israelites used the ram's horn as a battle signal; perhaps the best known instance was at the battle of Jericho, when the Lord said to Joshua: "You shall march around the city, all the men of war going around the city once. Thus you shall do for six days. And seven priests shall bear seven trumpets of rams' horns before the ark; and on the seventh day you shall march around the city seven times, the priests blowing the trumpets" (Josh. 6:3-4). The horn was also used to hold such liquids as oil—the wide end was blocked off and a hole drilled through the point. Samuel used this utensil to anoint David king after receiving the divine order: "Fill your horn with oil, and go!" (I Sam. 16:1).

SHEEP AND GOATS

Sheep and goats were commonly pastured together, and Hebrew has a word (*tson*) to denote this aggregate. But sheep were more valuable as well as more numerous than domesticated goats; for example, the rich man Nabal had three thousand sheep and one thousand goats (I Sam. 25:2), and in his prosperity Job owned fourteen thousand sheep (Job 42:12). When sheep and goats are used to represent humanity in the picture of the Last Judgment (Matt. 25:32), it may be that the sheep's higher commercial value had something to do with their representing those who are saved. Since large flocks of sheep always reflected considerable wealth, they became, in the picture language of the Hebrew prophets, symbols of prosperity and the bountiful blessings of God. To express the thriving existence that would be Israel's upon its return from Babylonia, Ezekiel made this comparison: "Like the flock at Jerusalem during her appointed feasts, so shall the waste cities be filled with flocks of men" (Ezek. 36:38).

Sheep originally lived on the steppes of central Asia, where, like the wild varieties that still exist there today, they were adept at climbing up and down the steep crags to search out grass and herbs growing among the rocks. But once the sheep was domesticated, its agility and speed disappeared. It became servile and dependent—in fact, almost helpless if left on its own.

LUXURIOUS GRASSLANDS

The sheep of Palestine fed on the grass of the meadows and the herbs of the hilly slopes. The luxurious grasslands of Gilead, Ammon, and Moab were the most important sheep-raising regions in biblical times. The meat of lambs from Bashan is mentioned in the Bible as an especially succulent delicacy provided by God for his people (Ezek. 39:18; Deut. 32:14). No wonder, then, that Mesha, a king of Moab (Bashan), specialized in sheep-breeding; his yearly tribute to Israel included a hundred thousand lambs and the wool of a hundred thousand rams (II Kings 3:4). The lambs were undoubtedly intended for butchering, but sheep were useful in so many ways that they were not only sold commercially, but were also ideal gifts of homage (as in II Chron. 17:11, when the Arabs were compelled to deliver a large number of rams and he-goats to King Jehoshaphat).

The first domesticated animal mentioned in the Bible is, appropriately, the sheep: "Now Abel was a keeper of the sheep" (Gen. 4:2). Most likely, its primary use in the early days of Israelite history was as a source of food. The large entourage at the court of King Solomon daily consumed "a hundred sheep," in addition to considerable game and poultry (I Kings 4:23). And although Nehemiah's household was no royal court, he nevertheless set an impressive table, for which "one ox and six choice sheep; fowls likewise" were prepared daily (Neh. 5:18). Milk was not an unimportant product of the sheep herds, for sheep's milk was a favorite beverage of the Israelites.

SHEEP'S WOOL

But wool was the main reason the sheep was considered so valuable by ancient people; cattle and goats could provide meat and milk, but not the clothing of high quality that could be spun and woven from sheep's wool. The shearing of sheep was, like the harvest, a great festival in Israel, one so highly regarded that even royalty were invited to partake in the celebration (II Sam. 13:23). The owner of a large flock supervised the shearing and also provided entertainment and food for the hired hands. When the tired and hungry messengers of David encountered Nabal, he was busy serving bread, wine, and meat to his shearers. "We come on a feast day," they said. "Pray, give whatever you have at hand to your servants and to your son David" (I Sam. 25:8); but the rich Nabal refused. When Rachel managed to spirit away her father's household gods, it was because Laban was out in the fields supervising the shearing (Gen. 31:19).

DOCILE WHILE SHEARED

The shearing was done in much the same way as it is today. The sheep was held down on its side and its legs were tied together; then it lay docilely while its wool was clipped. The suffering servant of the Lord is so pictured by Isaiah: "Like a sheep that before its shearers is dumb, so he opened not

This sculpture of the traditional Lamb of God symbol is from
the abbey church of the Benedictine monastery at Cluny,
France, which was founded in 910. (Photograph by Archives
Photographiques, Paris, from *The Horizon of Christianity;*
courtesy of the American Heritage Publishing Company.)

his mouth" (Isa. 53:7; cf. Acts 8:32). Only those sheep reserved for burnt offering were not shorn; there could be no question of holding back any part of the sacrifice from the Lord.

Before being used for clothing, the wool had to be processed. First it was washed—sometimes while still on the sheep —then carded and weighed for the market. The spinning of the wool was women's work. In the book of Proverbs there is a description of an able housewife who "puts her hands to the distaff, and her hands hold the spindle" (Prov. 31:19). The next step, weaving the spun thread into cloth on a loom, was primarily a man's occupation. The materials for the tabernacle and for the priests' garb were woven by chosen men highly skilled in their trade (Exod. 31:1-11; 35:35). In New Testament times, both Paul and Aquila were tent weavers by profession.

"Beware of false prophets," says Jesus, "who come to you in sheep's clothing but inwardly are ravenous wolves" (Matt. 7:15). "Sheep's clothing" here refers to wool garments, and Jesus was simply telling his listeners that a respectable outward appearance can conceal a wicked inner nature. A man wearing clothing of woven wool could be assumed to be at least fairly well off, but a person wearing the pelt of a sheep was probably poor—as was a wearer of goatskin.

LONELY LIFE OF SHEPHERD

Since the sheep was such an important part of the daily life of ancient peoples, it is understandable that the Bible dwells on the shepherd. The life of the lonely man tending his valuable charges was familiar to the writers of both the Old and New Testaments. The shepherd was necessarily a nomad, for the flock had to move from place to place to find forage. Often the shepherd was not, strictly speaking, the "leader" of his flock, but the follower: "I took you from the pasture, from following the sheep, that you should be prince over my people Israel," the Lord says to David (II Sam. 7:8). A shepherd would sometimes bring up the rear so that the weaker sheep and nursing ewes would not be left behind. Jacob, an experienced shepherd, tells his brother Esau: "My lord knows that the children are frail, and that the flocks and herds giving suck are a care to me; and if they are overdriven for one day, all the flocks will die" (Gen. 33:13; cf. Ps. 78: 70-72). Most of the time, though, the shepherd went before his dependent flock, leading it to "still waters" and "green pastures."

THE "GOOD SHEPHERD"

It was natural that the Israelites pictured a merciful God as the "shepherd" of his people: "The Lord is my shepherd, I shall not want" (Ps. 23:1). "He who has pity on them will lead them," says Isaiah about the marvelous return of the exiles, "and by springs of water will guide them" (Isa. 49:10). Thus Jesus' listeners knew what he meant when he called himself the Good Shepherd, the one who, "when he has brought out all his own . . . goes before them, and the sheep follow him" (John 10:4).

The good shepherd is a careful shepherd who knows his animals' needs and what can be expected of them. The young lamb he often carries in the breastfold of his cloak (Isa. 40:11). To such a man each sheep in his flock is important; in Ezekiel's mind God was such a shepherd, and he describes in some detail how He takes care of all his charges: "I myself will be the shepherd of my sheep, and I will make them lie down, says the Lord God. I will seek the lost, and I will bring back the strayed, and I will bind up the crippled, and I will strengthen the weak, and the fat and the strong I will watch over; I will feed them in justice" (Ezek. 34:15-16). The good shepherd also knew his obligations and his rights with respect to the owner of the flock. Since he was away with the sheep for long periods of time, he was allowed to use milk from the flock for his personal needs; Paul asks, rhetorically, when defending himself and Barnabas against the charge of living off their congregations: "Who tends a flock without getting some of the milk?" (I Cor. 9:7). Apparently, though, the shepherd did not have the right to kill any of his sheep for meat; in maintaining that he had served his master well, Jacob tells Laban that in twenty years he never did this (Gen. 31:38).

RIGOROUS STEADFASTNESS

In fact, Jacob's words to Laban give us our best picture of how rigorous was the life of a shepherd in biblical times: "These twenty years I have been with you; your ewes and your she-goats have not miscarried, and I have not eaten the rams of your flocks. That which was torn by wild beasts I did not bring to you; I bore the loss of it myself; of my hand you required it, whether stolen by day or stolen by night. Thus I was; by day the heat consumed me, and the cold by night, and my sleep fled from my eyes" (Gen. 31:38-40). When Hebrew writers compared God to a shepherd, then, they were aware that being a shepherd entailed suffering for the sake of the flock; surely Jesus had this suffering and steadfastness in mind when he called himself the Good Shepherd (John 10:11).

SLINGSHOT AND STAFF

The story of David and Goliath (I Samuel 17) gives us an idea of how a shepherd in ancient times might be equipped. Arriving at the Israelite camp, David carried a shepherd's bag, a slingshot, and a staff. He put stones for the slingshot in the bag when he went out to face Goliath, but this bag was generally used for carrying provisions. It was a large leather container, usually made from goatskin, and could be used for carrying liquids, like a canteen. Both the staff and the sling were defensive weapons, although the staff was also used simply as a walking stick. At close range the staff was used to fend off wild animals, dogs, and if need be, people who were preying on the flock; the slingshot was effective at a longer range, as Goliath found out too late.

The scarcity of springs in Palestine made the watering of the flock a crucial problem for the shepherd. When Abraham and Lot apportioned Canaan for their people and flocks, Lot, who had first choice, selected the region around the Jordan and its tributaries (Gen. 13:10-11), thereby securing not only ample grazing land, but also easily accessible and abundant sources of drinking water.

To protect the flock at night against predatory attacks, the shepherd tried to provide a "fold." In meadows near villages folds were built and watchmen hired to relieve the shepherds. Not everyone could afford these luxuries, and in the Nativity story the shepherds were "out in the field, keeping watch over their flock by night" (Luke 2:8). Probably they had set up a tent for shelter, consisting simply of goat's-hair blankets spread across sapling supports. In more rugged terrain, a shepherd could find an enclosure of rocks or a cave that would serve as a fold for his flock. During his pursuit of David, Saul "came to the sheepfolds by the way, where there was a cave" (I Sam. 24:3) and took shelter there.

STRIPED, SPECKLED, SPOTTED

One of the most curious incidents in the Bible in which sheep play a part is found in Genesis, where Jacob is said to have been working as Laban's shepherd. At Jacob's suggestion, they had agreed that Jacob's wages should consist of those goats in the flock that were spotted and those sheep that had black wool. Since both of these colorings were rare, Laban obviously felt that he would be getting cheap labor, but Jacob had some interesting ideas about husbandry and breeding. He "took fresh rods of poplar and almond and plane, and peeled white streaks in them, exposing the white

of the rods. He set the rods which he had peeled in front of
... the watering troughs, where the flocks came to drink. And
since they bred when they came to drink, the flocks bred in
front of the rods and so the flocks brought forth striped,
speckled, and spotted" (Gen. 30:37-39). Although this method
would not convince a modern geneticist, in this case it apparently had the desired effect. Jacob used a more orthodox
method of assuring himself the pick of the flock: he set up
the rods only when the stronger animals were breeding (v. 41).
Lambs are born at two different times during the year, in

With stately tread the tribute-bearers of Persepolis offer the
Persian king two of the most valuable gifts that could be
brought in ancient times, a pair of rams. Note the down-
curving horns and the heavy tails which mark these as "fat-
tailed sheep." (Photograph courtesy of the Oriental Institute
of the University of Chicago.)

November and June; the former are called "early" lambs, the latter "late" lambs. Jacob knew that the stronger animals were those which bred in summer and gave birth to the better stock, the early lambs.

"MOTHER SHEEP"

It should be mentioned, finally, that the Israelites did not consider the sheep just a useful commodity, but considered it a beautiful animal. The word "sheep" had no degrading or jocular connotations. The name of Jacob's wife was Rachel, which means "mother sheep." Possibly some Israelites even kept lambs in their houses as pets. In the speech in which he confronts David with his crime against Uriah, the prophet Nathan says: "The poor man had nothing but one little ewe lamb, which he had bought. And he brought it up, and it grew up with him and his children; it used to eat of his morsel, and drink from his cup, and lie in his bosom, and it was like a daughter to him" (II Sam. 12:3-4). The touching picture drawn by Nathan was meant to impress David with the fact that when he took Bathsheba from her husband he had been as cruel as the person who had seized the poor man's lamb.

WHITE AS WOOL

The whiteness of wool fascinated many writers of the Bible: "Though your sins are like scarlet, they shall be white as snow; though they are red like crimson, they shall become like wool" (Isa. 1:18; cf. Ps. 147:16; Dan. 7:9; Rev. 1:14). Probably the most startling poetic image is in the Song of Solomon: "Your teeth are like a flock of ewes, that have come up from the washing, all of them bear twins, not one among them is bereaved" (Song of Sol. 6:6).

The Small Rodents

"And these are unclean to you among the swarming things that swarm upon the earth: the weasel, the mouse . . ." (Lev. 11:29). The Mosaic prohibition against eating mice was a very rigid one; only pagans would break this law. Those who would eat "the abomination and mice, shall come to an end together, says the Lord" (Isa. 66:17).

The Hebrew word *akbar*, which is always rendered "mouse" in our Bibles, is probably a catch-all term for a variety of small rodents. The order Rodentia has more species, by far, than any other order of mammals, and the student of zoology is confronted by a bewildering variety of rodents, many of which are identified only by their Latin classification names. The task assigned to Adam in the Garden of Eden, to name

CLASSIFICATION. *Jaculus jaculus* (Egyptian jerboa), member of Dipodidae family; *Psammomys obesus* (fat sand rat), member of Gerbillinae subfamily, Muridae family (Old World rats and mice); *Mesocricetus auratus* (golden hamster), member of Cricetinae subfamily, Muridae family; *Arvicola amphibius* (water vole), member of Microtinae subfamily, Muridae family; all four of order Rodentia.

LEXICON. *Hebrew:* AKBAR.

all the living creatures, is overwhelming when one approaches the rodents. No less than twenty-three different kinds of small rodents (that is, mice, rats, and their close relatives) have been found in the fairly small area of Palestine. Assuming that most of these were present in biblical times, we can see that the prohibition in Leviticus excluded quite a number of meat dishes from Israelite tables.

AN EDIBLE RODENT

Nor is this as easy an instruction to follow as it might appear to be. Naturally, few of us ever entertain the notion of eating rats or mice, although in some areas the larger rodents such as raccoons and squirrels are considered a delicacy. However, among the Arabs in the Near East certain rodents, namely, those belonging to the group called gerbils, are a favorite food. These creatures live in the desert sand, or in rubble heaps and thickets. A typical example would be the fat sand rat, native to Egypt in particular, which is some eight inches long, with a fairly short tail that has a thick covering of hair and a tassel at the tip. The fur is a rather attractive reddish brown with black spots on the back, and on the sides and belly the fur turns to light yellow. The fat sand rat burrows under the ground, but also moves freely in the open, even during the daytime.

A LEAPING RODENT

People of the ancient Near East were probably also familiar with the Egyptian jerboa. It has been said of this animal that it has the head of a hare, the whiskers of a squirrel, the nose of a swine, the body and forelegs of a mouse, the hind legs of a bird, and the tail of a lion. By not taking any of these comparisons too literally one can get a pretty good picture of the jerboa. It is larger than the common rat, with a body more than seven inches long and a tail of eight inches. Its hind legs, which are six times as long as its forelegs, en-

The Egyptians were close observers of animal life. This highly realistic mouse nibbling on a morsel was fashioned of bronze and actually was modeled to scale, standing only a couple of inches high. (Photograph courtesy of the Oriental Institute of the University of Chicago.)

able it to take long kangaroo-like leaps and to travel much faster than a man can. Other characteristic features are its large eyes, its long rabbit-like ears, its unusually long whiskers, its soft, sand-colored fur which turns to white on the belly, and the black-and-white tassel at the tip of its tail. The Egyptian jerboa is native to Palestine, Arabia, and Egypt. A very shy animal, it is rarely seen. It burrows in hard, sandy soil in deserted areas, where it feeds on both plants and insects.

Another distinctive small rodent of the Palestine area is

Three of the more unusual kinds of small rodent common to the Near East are shown here in typical poses: from the bottom, the golden hamster, the water vole, and the Egyptian jerboa. Note the muskrat-like appearance of the water vole, in contrast to the delicate features of the agile jerboa. (Drawing by Carol Wilde.)

the golden hamster. Found mostly in Syria today, it is another rodent that supplies food for the Arabs. It is a little smaller than the common hamster, but it has a longer tail and silky, golden fur. Although attractive, it is somewhat of a pest, feeding on peas, beans, seed, and grain. During the fall it busily collects food which it carries back to the nest in its large cheek pouches. An accomplished excavator, the golden hamster burrows from three to six feet below the surface of the earth, where each animal occupies its own "apartment" consisting of a living room and storage chamber. In spite of its clumsy build it can move with great speed and is able to climb.

A PLAGUE OF WATER VOLES

In the First Book of Samuel it is related that the Philistines had confiscated the ark of the covenant and had set it up in the temple of Dagon at Ashdod. As punishment for this act, the country of the Philistines was hit by a series of plagues, during one of which the land was overrun by mice. Perhaps these were simply common field mice, which are also found in Palestine, but they may also have been water voles, sometimes called water rats. Although these creatures are found all over Europe and in the greater part of Asia, they often appear in the Syria-Palestine area in large swarms. The water vole is about six inches long with a tail of some four inches, has a rather short nose and small ears, and is dark brown. It builds a complicated system of long underground passages, usually close to water, and feeds on plants from underneath the ground. In satisfying its hunger it can do considerable damage, and can even gnaw through young trees of up to three or four inches in diameter.

In order to lift the plague that was ravaging their country, the Philistines were advised to return the ark to the Israelites and to send along, as a penitential offering for the theft, five mice fashioned of gold (I Sam. 6:4).

The Swine

Of all the animals specified as unclean in the Pentateuch, the most renowned is unquestionably the swine. The original instructions are quite explicit: "And the swine, because it parts the hoof and is cloven-footed but does not chew the cud, is unclean to you. Of their flesh you shall not eat, and their carcasses you shall not touch; they are unclean to you" (Lev. 11:7-8; Deut. 14:8).

Commonly known in this country as the pig (although technically this term applies to a newborn swine), the many breeds of domestic swine are of the same species as the wild boar. The length of the swine varies from four to six feet, and the average shoulder height is three feet. The thick layer of fat just under the skin is especially pronounced in domestic breeds. Although clumsily built, the swine is quite lively and can move with agility and speed—as many an unsuspecting visitor to a farm has discovered to his surprise.

Wherever it is mentioned in the Bible, its less pleasant characteristics are emphasized. One reason may be that the Israelites were originally a nomadic people, who had little use for

---

CLASSIFICATION. *Sus scrofa* (domestic swine), member of Suidae family of order Artiodactyla (even-toed hoofed animals).
LEXICON. *Hebrew:* CHAZIR. *Greek:* CHOIROS. Also, HUS (sow).

---

an animal so closely associated with the settled life. Whatever one believes about the swine's desirability as food, however, it must be admitted that it is not an especially attractive creature when it is alive. It will eat anything, vegetable or animal—rats, snakes, insects, even carrion. There are instances of adult males indulging in cannibalism and, more frequently, of sows eating their entire litter as soon as the pigs are born. Swine are unrestrainably greedy, and a common farmyard sight is of swine struggling fiercely for a place not only next to, but in, the feed trough.

PRODIGAL SON

Not the least unpleasant of its characteristics is the almost unbearable odor of its excrement, an odor that clings to those who tend swine; swineherds can be identified from a long way off. Thus, when Jesus wanted to show the extent of the degradation to which the prodigal son of his parable had fallen, he had him become a swineherd. Even so, when the prodigal son returned to his father's home, "while he was yet at a distance, his father saw him and had compassion, and ran and embraced him and kissed him" (Luke 15:20). Jesus vividly shows how great and incomprehensible is the love of God for man; God does not hesitate to receive and embrace the sinner.

WASHED TO WALLOW

"It has happened to them," says Peter about false teachers, "according to the true proverb . . . the sow is washed only to wallow in the mire" (II Pet. 2:22). Everyone who has visited a farm has seen swine rolling in the mud, and for the biblical writers they came to represent the epitome of dirtiness and ugliness. "Do not throw your pearls before swine," says Jesus, "lest they trample them underfoot and turn to attack you" (Matt. 7:6). The beauty and value of pearls are of no use to swine, who would only think of them as something to eat—finding this not to be the case, they would turn on the one who, from their point of view, had cheated them of food. The meaning of Jesus' cryptic statement is a bit clearer when seen in this light: there is no use in hoping that everyone—especially those who live a "swinelike" existence, mired in their own greed and self-interest—will automatically be attracted to the beauty of divine truth.

An older biblical example of how the beauty of an object is contrasted with the ugliness of the swine appears in Proverbs: "Like a gold ring in a swine's snout is a beautiful woman without discretion" (Prov. 11:22).

PORK-EATING NEIGHBORS

Although the Israelites did not breed swine, their neighbors, unrestricted by their own religions, raised swine on a large scale both for food and for sacrificial purposes. For example, an Egyptian prince at the beginning of the Eighteenth Dynasty (ca. 1550 B.C.) is recorded as owning a herd of fifteen hundred swine.

The Israelites did not always resist the temptations posed by their pork-eating neighbors, and during the Babylonian Captivity they apparently participated in pagan sacrificial feasts and ate the flesh of the swine: "I spread out my hands all the day to a rebellious people, who walk in a way that is not good, following their own devices; a people who provoke me to my face continually . . . who eat swine's flesh, and broth of abominable things is in their vessels" (Isa. 65:2-4; cf. Isa. 66:3, 17). Later, however, the Jews who were ruled by Antiochus Epiphanes in the second century B.C. were willing to suffer the anguishing death of martyrs rather than obey Antiochus when he sought to force them to eat swine's flesh. The story is told in the Apocrypha, in the first book of Maccabees.

There is no evidence that would lead us to believe that swine were raised in Palestine during the time of Jesus, although pork-raising had been developed to a high level

It may seem strange to see the prodigal son in a late medieval farmyard, but to Albrecht Dürer, who made this engraving, the story was just as applicable in 1500 as in A.D. 30. The swine depicted here closely resemble wild boar, probably the only variety of swine known to the artist. (Photograph courtesy of the Art Institute of Chicago.)

in Roman agriculture. The prodigal son tended swine in an unnamed foreign country, and the great herd of swine into which Jesus drove the unclean spirits was encountered in the land of the Gerasenes, a non-Jewish municipality east of the Jordan (Mark 5:11-13).

The Wildcat

One will not find the wildcat mentioned by name in the standard versions of our English Bible. Yet there is little doubt that the particular variety known as the European wildcat was common to Palestine and familiar to biblical authors. One of the Hebrew words usually translated simply as "wild beast" probably has a more specific meaning, and, for the purposes of this book, we can assume that its meaning is "wildcat."

Resembling the common domesticated tabby cat, but not its direct ancestor as was formerly supposed, the wildcat is considerably larger. It is about two feet long, and its powerful, bushy tail adds another foot to the overall measurement. Its shoulder height is about twenty inches, and it weighs as

---

CLASSIFICATION. *Felis sylvestris* (European wildcat), member of Felidae family (cats) of order Carnivora (flesh-eating mammals).
LEXICON. *Hebrew:* TSIYYIM.

---

much as fifteen pounds. The heavy fur is grayish with a black stripe running down the middle of the back and black transverse stripes on the flanks; the belly is yellowish-gray with black spots.

No domestic cat is mentioned in the Bible, for any beast of prey was regarded by the Israelites as unclean; not only would it not be eaten, but it would be inconceivable for any unclean beast to be kept in the home.

A SOLITARY CREATURE

Widely distributed today in mountainous regions of central and southern Europe and in Asia Minor, the wildcat is found in dense evergreen forests and especially in wooded cliffs and mountains, where it can easily find safe hiding places among the rocks. It is a solitary animal, seeking company only during the mating period. As soon as kittens are old enough to fend for themselves, they leave the mother. For its relatively small size, the wildcat is a fierce and dangerous creature, which preys primarily on mice, rats, squirrels, and small birds, but may also attack newborn calves and large birds such as pheasants. A typical nocturnal hunter, it keeps itself hidden during the day and feels most at home in regions completely deserted by human beings.

FOND OF DESOLATE PLACES

Wherever the wildcat is mentioned in the Bible, it is its fondness for deserted places that is emphasized. Both Isaiah and Jeremiah mention the wildcat to express complete desolation. Isaiah declares that Babylon "will never be inhabited. . . . But [wildcats] will lie down there, and its houses will be full of howling creatures" (Isa. 13:21; cf. Isa. 34:14). Jeremiah prophesies the destruction of Babylon in the same vein: "Therefore [wildcats] and jackals shall dwell in Babylon . . . ; she shall be peopled no more for ever, nor inhabited for all generations" (Jer. 50:39).

117

In ancient Egypt the Nubian (or Egyptian) cat was domesticated. Apparently a part of temple worship, it was regarded with a great deal of reverence, and embalmed cat mummies, pictures, and statuettes have been discovered in ancient Egyptian ruins. This bronze statuette is from the Twenty-second Dynasty (*ca.* 900 B.C.). (Photograph courtesy of the University Museum, Philadelphia.)

The Wolf

Like the swine, the wolf has come to stand for a very definite characteristic: when we hear its name, the word "ravenous" comes immediately to mind. Part of this attitude stems from well-known passages of the Bible, for the wolf was a common beast of prey in Palestine in ancient times. It is still found there today, as well as in many places in Asia Minor. One of the most widely distributed predatory animals, it is also found in Europe, North America, and throughout Asia, although in much smaller numbers than formerly.

From nose to rump the wolf measures about three feet, and its drooping tail is about eighteen inches long. It looks like a rather skinny German Shepherd dog. The grayish-yellow pelt is coarse and short-haired. The wolf is always on the move; hunger drives it from place to place in constant search of new hunting grounds. During spring and fall wolves usually roam singly or in pairs, whereas in summer they may travel in family groups, and in winter several of these groups may join to form a large pack. Hunger and greed combine to

---

CLASSIFICATION. *Canis lupus lupus* (European wolf), member of Canidae family (wolves, true dogs, jackals, and foxes) of order Carnivora (flesh-eating mammals).

LEXICON. *Hebrew:* ZEEB. *Greek:* LUKOS.

---

hominif fimulantē. Cui corex in uuno mifla dat
bibendū ppē uarias infirmitates. Corp̄ ū p̄xxx.
annos caute colligit ad multas infirmitates
medendas. et foporan dolore ñ fentiunt. huius
fpecies due. femina: cuiuf folia lactuce funt
fimilia: mala generat in fimilitudinem pruna
rum. Ofafculus: foliis bete fimilibus.

upus grēca diruuatione in linguā nr̄am
tranffert. lupos ꝋ dicunt illi licos. Licos aū
grece a morfib; appellant. q̄ rabie rapacita
tis quecg inuenerint truciant dñi lupos
uocatos aiunt quafi leopos q̄ q̄fi leonib;

"Fierce wolves will come in among you, not sparing the flock,"
says Paul, and this manuscript illumination from a twelfth-
century A.D. English bestiary shows a wolf threatening the
cowering sheep. Medieval artists were not always careful of
zoological details, but this one was familiar enough with the
wolf to show its drooping tail and slouching pose. (Photograph
courtesy of the Pierpont Morgan Library.)

make wolves absolutely fearless, and they will not hesitate to approach people or inhabited places if the need arises. They feed on large game animals such as deer, which does not make them favorites of hunters.

"WOLVES AT DARK"

Palestinian shepherds of old fought many a bloody battle with wolves that plundered their flocks. Since wolves will usually remain concealed during the day and come out in search of food at dusk, biblical authors often refer to them as "evening wolves" or "wolves at dark." For instance, Habakkuk calls the Chaldeans "more fierce than evening wolves" (Hab. 1:8), for they were a warlike tribe that traveled far and wide to rob and plunder. The wicked judges of Jerusalem are called "evening wolves that leave nothing till the morning" (Zeph. 3:3) by the indignant prophet Zephaniah. Obviously he had in mind the proverbial greed and savagery of the wolf, which would eat gluttonously throughout the night and then sleep through the daylight hours. Thus when Jeremiah issued his threatening prophecy that "a wolf from the desert shall destroy" the sinful inhabitants of Jerusalem (Jer. 5:6), those who listened to him understood at once how dread a punishment this was. "Her princes in the midst of her are like wolves tearing the prey," says Ezekiel. They are anxious to shed blood, "destroying lives to get dishonest gain" (Ezek. 22:27).

TRIBE OF BENJAMIN

When the patriarch Jacob was on his deathbed and, in the course of his blessing, was describing the attributes of the tribes of his descendants, he characterized Benjamin, the son of Rachel, as a wolf: "Benjamin is a ravenous wolf, in the morning devouring the prey, and at even dividing the spoil" (Gen. 49:27). Therefore, this tribe would be known for its fearlessness and unbridled cruelty: there was something of the wolf's nature in the Benjaminite King Saul, and even in another Benjaminite, the Apostle Paul.

WITHIN THE FOLD

New Testament references to wolves are almost always connected with sheep, the wolf representing those who would destroy the "flock," the community of believers. "The wolf snatches them and scatters them," says Jesus (John 10:12), and again, to his disciples: "Behold, I send you out as sheep in the midst of wolves" (Matt. 10:16). Paul uses the same kind of language: "I know that after my departure fierce wolves will come in among you, not sparing the flock" (Acts 20:29). The implication is that these "wolves" would appear as presumably loyal members of the congregation and not be immediately recognizable for what they were. For Jesus had said: "Beware of false prophets, who come to you in sheep's clothing but inwardly are ravenous wolves" (Matt. 7:15). Statements such as these would dispel any illusions about the church being immune to rapaciousness and greed, and in fact the history of Christianity is amply provided with instances of wolves preying on the sheep from within the fold.

Birds

The Bittern

A wary, solitary bird that spends the daylight hours skulking among swamp reeds, the bittern is a member of the heron family. It does not possess the beauty and grace of its heron cousins, however; its very short neck is covered with long, soft feathers which make the neck seem disproportionately heavy, and its legs are relatively short. A partially migratory bird, it is found everywhere in Europe, Asia, and Africa, and related species thrive in America and Australia.

Like other members of the heron family, the bittern builds its nest amid reed thickets on lake shores, near backwaters, and in swamps. With its mottled and barred brown and black coloring, it is very difficult to distinguish from its surroundings. But what can easily be detected is its distinctive voice— a rather sinister, powerful call emitted by the male, especially in the mating season. First come two or three subdued grunting notes, followed by a "woomp" that sounds at a distance like a watchman's horn and may be heard from a mile away.

The few places where it is mentioned in the Bible, the bittern evokes a scene of mystery and eeriness, which is to be expected, for this bird is active only in the darkness, and

CLASSIFICATION. *Botaurus stellaris* (European bittern), member of Botaurinae subfamily of Ardeidae family of order Ciconiiformes.
LEXICON. *Hebrew:* QIPPOD.

A solitary bittern stands in the reeds of a swamp, its typical habitat. (Photograph courtesy of the Chicago Natural History Museum.)

the frightening sound of its weird call is magnified at night. Isaiah, speaking of Babylon, says: "I will also make it a possession for the bittern" (Isa. 14:23, KJV). And of Edom he says: "The cormorant and bittern shall possess it" (Isa. 34:11, KJV). Since the bittern is shy and shuns inhabited places, the prophet is emphasizing that the cities will be devoid of human life. Again, Zephaniah, testifying to the judgment upon Nineveh, says: "The bittern shall lodge in the upper lintels of it" (Zeph. 2:14, KJV). The once prosperous city shall become as desolate as a lonely swamp, and its once busy streets will echo with the bittern's evening cry.

The Chicken

"O Jerusalem, Jerusalem, killing the prophets and stoning those who are sent to you! How often would I have gathered your children together as a hen gathers her brood under her wings, and you would not!" (Matt. 23:37; Luke 13:34).

This charming picture of the hen calling her chicks and spreading her wings to protect them against danger during the day and against the cold at night appears in one of the best-known sayings of Jesus. As he approaches Jerusalem for the last time, the city where he will be crucified, he laments its fate. Coming from a rural area, he was familiar with common farmyard sights and often referred to them.

There is little doubt that the chicken was a common domesticated bird in New Testament times. The cock is mentioned several times in the Gospels, especially with reference to its service as a "timepiece." A rooster habitually crows an hour or two before dawn; and so in ancient times the third watch of the night, from midnight to 3 A.M., was commonly known as the "cockcrow." Accordingly, Jesus says in his parable about the master returning from a journey: "You do not know

---

CLASSIFICATION. *Gallus gallus* (common domestic fowl), member of Phasianidae family of order Galliformes.

LEXICON. *Hebrew:* ZARZIR (?). *Greek:* ALEKTOR (cock); ORNIS (hen); NOSSION (nestling).

when the master of the house will come, in the evening, or at midnight, or at cockcrow, or in the morning" (Mark 13:35). And on the eve of the crucifixion, he warns Peter in a well-known passage: "Truly, I say to you, this very night, before the cock crows, you will deny me three times" (Matt. 26:34).

"FOWL"

In the Old Testament there are a number of references to a "fowl" used for food. It is possible, but only barely so, that the chicken is meant here; usually the word "fowl" in the King James Version of the Old Testament means winged creatures in general—the "fowl of the air"—while the term "fatted fowl" most likely means "goose." If chickens were raised by the Israelites, one would expect some mention of this fact. They were raised, for many centuries, in such neighboring lands as Mesopotamia, Egypt, and Greece.

Every day during the rebuilding of Jerusalem, Nehemiah entertained one hundred fifty Jews as well as visiting officials from neighboring nations; and "one ox and six choice sheep; fowls likewise" provided the fare (Neh. 5:18). If chickens are meant here, and if we assume that they were not as yet raised locally, then possibly they were provided by the visiting officials. There is one piece of external evidence that chickens were known in Palestine in the sixth century B.C.: a seal has been unearthed that bears a picture of a fighting game cock and the inscription: "Belonging to Jaazaniah, servant of the king." Jaazaniah is mentioned in II Kings 25:23 as one of the Jews left behind in Palestine at the time of the Babylonian Exile. In Prov. 30:31 reference is made to a "strutting cock," but the meaning of the Hebrew here is not clear: "wrestler" may be meant, in which case "strutting cock"— the Greek interpretation in the Septuagint—would have been intended figuratively.

According to the Talmud, keeping chickens was prohibited in Jerusalem in New Testament times to prevent the insects and larvae that breed in chicken droppings from contaminating sacrificial flesh. The cock Peter heard apparently belonged to the Romans living there, or perhaps not, since many Jews at the time had adopted Greek and Roman ways and would not have felt constrained by such a regulation.

Peter hears the cry of a rooster as he lingers before a warming fire in the courtyard while his Master is being interrogated by the high priest on the eve of the crucifixion. Behind him stand his accusers. The illumination is from a fourteenth-century Hungarian manuscript. (Photograph courtesy of the Pierpont Morgan Library.)

The Crane

A handsome and stately creature, the crane is the second largest bird found in Palestine, standing at a height of more than three feet. (The largest bird is the ostrich.) Sometimes confused with the heron, the crane is distinguished by its greater size and the drooping black feathers that form its "tail." The overall color is steel gray, and the head and neck are black with a longitudinal white stripe; the smooth crown of the head is bright pink.

Both times that the crane is mentioned in the Bible it is listed with other birds in connection with some trait each shares. Jeremiah declares: "Even the stork in the heavens knows her times; and the turtledove, swallow, and crane keep the time of their coming; but my people know not the ordinance of the Lord" (Jer. 8:7). These are all migratory

---

CLASSIFICATION. *Grus grus* (European crane), member of Gruidae family of order Gruiformes.

LEXICON. *Hebrew:* AGUR.

birds, whose instincts justly evoke wonder in this thoughtful observer. Comparing the unerring obedience of the creature to its inner promptings with the inability of man to listen to his conscience, the prophet is dismayed at the wilfulness of his fellow human beings.

"I CLAMOR . . ."

Isaiah, marking a different trait, refers to the distinctive voice of the crane: "Like a swallow or a crane I clamor. . . . O Lord, I am oppressed" (Isa. 38:14). The crane is known for the trumpet-like call it emits, a strident "krooh." In addition, it hisses and makes guttural noises, all of which certainly add up to a "clamor," especially one that expresses both sorrow and distress.

BEAUTY NOT MENTIONED

In view of the general appreciation of animal beauty in the Bible, it is somewhat surprising that neither prophet mentions the striking beauty and elegance of cranes, especially when they fly in formation. With calm and sure movements, often at an altitude that makes them difficult to discern with the naked eye, cranes begin their journey north from Africa to eastern Europe and Scandinavia in March and April. They prefer to fly during the day, in flocks of up to a hundred arranged in V-formation; the stronger birds take turns leading the flock to its destination. Undoubtedly it was during this time of migration that they could most easily be observed in Palestine.

On the ground the crane is very shy and alert, making it difficult for a person to get close to it. It lives mainly in swamps, and in Palestine today it can be found in the regions of Beersheba, one of the few areas in the southern part of the country where there is abundant water. Primarily a vegetarian, the crane feeds on grass and grain, but may also devour insects and snakes.

The Dove
The Turtledove

In ancient Palestine there was an abundance of doves of many species, and the dove, the turtledove, and the pigeon are mentioned often in the Bible. One of the earliest birds to be domesticated by man, the dove was used as food and also in temple sacrifices. The word "dove" is used loosely for the smaller members of the Columbidae family, while "pigeon" usually refers to the larger members. "Turtledove" is used for all species in the *Streptopelia* genus of the same family.

The dove most commonly found in the wild state was the rock dove, which keeps to rocky regions, where it builds its nest in gorges, crevices, and old ruins. Jeremiah refers to the inaccessibility of its nest when he uses it as an example of a safe refuge for those who are being pursued: "Leave the cities, and dwell in the rock, O inhabitants of Moab! Be like the dove that nests in the sides of the mouth of a gorge"

CLASSIFICATION. *Columba livia* (rock dove or pigeon) and *Streptopelia turtur turtur* (turtledove), members of Columbidae family of order Columbiformes.

LEXICON. Dove, pigeon—*Hebrew:* YONAH (dove); GOZAL (pigeon). *Greek:* PERISTERA. Turtledove—*Hebrew:* TOR. *Greek:* TRUGON.

(Jer. 48:28). At the present time the rock dove is found primarily in the area around the Sea of Galilee and, farther to the south, in the numerous ravines leading down to the Dead Sea. Its nests are poorly constructed; eggs are hatched twice a year, the brooding period lasting from fourteen to twenty days, during which time the male and female take turns sitting on the nest.

"FLY LIKE A CLOUD"

The domestic pigeon, which is seen in such abundance today in cities, is descended from the rock pigeon. It also thrived in Jerusalem, even in Old Testament times. Isaiah asks: "Who are these that fly like a cloud, and like doves to their windows?" (Isa. 60:8). Here "windows" probably means the latticed framework of the pigeon coops used at the time, for the Hebrew word for "coop" is literally "lattice." In New Testament times there were many such pigeon coops in the park surrounding the palace of Herod the Great in Jerusalem, according to the Jewish historian Josephus (*The Jewish Wars*, Bk. 5, IV, 4).

"VOICE OF THE TURTLEDOVE"

The turtledove, a migratory bird that appears regularly in Palestine in the early part of April, was seen as a harbinger of spring by a Hebrew poet: "Lo, the winter is past. . . . and the voice of the turtledove is heard in our land" (Song of Sol. 2:11-12). And Jeremiah says: "The turtledove, swallow, and crane keep the time of their coming" (Jer. 8:7). The turtledove was also important to the Israelites as a sacrificial animal. Easy to raise, and therefore a common source of food for the poor, it was used in both the burnt offering and the sin offering. Even as early as the time of Abraham it is mentioned along with the pigeon as an acceptable sacrifice (Gen. 15:9). After her confinement was over an Israelite woman was expected to offer a turtledove or a young pigeon as a sin offering (Lev. 12:6). Whereas more affluent people might offer a yearling lamb, the sacrifice of Joseph and Mary when they presented the child Jesus at the temple consisted of two turtledoves. This offering was in accordance with the law, for "if [the woman who has been confined] cannot afford a lamb, then she shall take two turtledoves or two young pigeons, one for a burnt offering and the other for a sin offering" (Lev. 12:8).

But the turtledove could mean much more than merely the sacrificial offering of the poor man; to one of the psalmists, Israel is the turtledove of God, and he prays: "O Lord . . . do not deliver the soul of thy dove to the wild beasts" (Ps. 74:18-19).

LOVEBIRDS

The many references to the characteristics of the dove provide us with some of the loveliest and most picturesque passages of the Bible, and once again allow us to appreciate the biblical authors' powers of observation. Most of us are familiar with the sight of a pair of doves performing their charming love play, or at least with the phrase "lovebirds." It is only natural that the author of the biblical love poem, the Song of Solomon, should borrow some of his images from this ritual. The bridegroom calls his beloved "my dove." He compares her radiant eyes to doves (Song of Sol. 1:15), and she returns the compliment: "His eyes are like doves beside springs of water" (Song of Sol. 5:12). The dove was such a charming and highly regarded bird that its name was used for women; thus Job called one of his daughters Jemimah, "the dove" (Job 42:14). One Hebrew poet describes a dove whose glories surpass those of the common species when he speaks of "the wings of a dove covered with silver, its pinions with green gold" (Ps. 68:13).

The dove is often a symbol of simplicity for biblical writers, a defenseless creature that does no harm to others. The gentle disposition of the dove was undoubtedly present in Jesus' mind when he said to his disciples: "So be . . . innocent as doves" (Matt. 10:16). Not only is the dove poorly equipped to defend itself, but it is also subject to panic and is quite likely to fly right into the snares of its enemies. Thus the prophet says: "Ephraim is like a dove, silly and without sense, calling to Egypt, going to Assyria" (Hos. 7:11), aptly describing Judah's policy of playing off the two powers against each other—a policy the prophets frequently condemned.

LAMENTING LIKE A DOVE

In the ears of many biblical authors the cooing of the dove often sounded like human laments and sighs. "Like a swallow or a crane I clamor, I moan like a dove," says Isaiah (38:14); and again: "We moan and moan like doves" (Isa. 59:11). Likewise, Nahum speaks of "moaning like doves, and beating their breasts" (Nah. 2:7). Ezekiel, speaking of the judgment of the Lord, gives us this striking image: "And if any survivors escape, they will be on the mountains, like doves of the valleys, all of them moaning, every one over his iniquity" (Ezek. 7:16).

NOAH'S SCOUTS

The great speed and endurance of the dove in flight (a carrier pigeon has been clocked at 110 miles an hour on a twenty-minute flight, and most can fly for fifteen hours without stopping) are also noted. Thus the poet, hard pressed by his enemies, says with a sigh: "O that I had wings like a dove! I would fly away and be at rest" (Ps. 55:6). Since the dove became associated with human beings very early in history, its flying ability, homing instincts, and skill in finding its direction were probably known even to the most ancient civilizations—Noah sent out doves to be his "scouts" when he was stranded on Mount Ararat. They could range over a wide area and would be liable to return to their home base. And,

A familiar Christian symbol, the dove in this manuscript illumination represents the Holy Spirit. The scene is the Annunciation, with Mary and Gabriel, as they appear in a fifteenth-century Flemish "Hours of the Virgin." (Photograph courtesy of the Pierpont Morgan Library.)

in fact, the second dove released at sunrise returned before the day was over with a freshly plucked olive leaf in its beak (Gen. 8:8-11).

SYMBOLIZES HOLY SPIRIT

In the New Testament the dove is often used as a symbol of the Holy Spirit, a fact which undoubtedly has something to do with its earlier associations with the qualities of purity, innocence, and love. It may also be significant that the dove was the only bird used in Jewish sacrificial worship. In the Gospel according to John, at the time of the baptism of Jesus, John the Baptist testified: "I saw the Spirit descend as a dove from heaven" (John 1:32). The next day he said of Jesus: "Behold, the Lamb of God!" (John 1:36). Both the dove and the lamb, as the most common sacrifices of the people of the time, carry with them strong connotations of the atoning role that Jesus was to play.

The dove has been a symbol of the Holy Spirit in Christian art from the earliest periods of the church down to the present. The dove can also represent a human soul that has entered its eternal rest; hence one can often find the image of a dove with an olive branch on tombstones. In graveyards of the ancient church, lamps in the shape of doves have been found. Some Christian art depicts the twelve apostles as twelve doves surrounding a cross. Above many baptismal fonts appears a representation of a dove, obviously in reference to John 1:32. A flying dove was, during the patristic period, a symbol of both the ascension of Christ and the martyr's passage to his eternal home. The picture of a dove in the act of drinking represents the soul being refreshed by the Eucharist. The bread of the Eucharist has sometimes been kept in a dove-shaped vessel made of precious metals and suspended above the altar, or preserved in a box the shape of a dovecot. Today the dove is still a common Christian symbol.

The Eagle

Eagles are found all over the world, living at various altitudes, although a majority of species prefer forested areas. Some, however, seek out the mountainous wastelands, the steppes, or the deserts. The eagle is tautly and powerfully built, with strong wings; every movement it makes reveals suppleness and strength. Its distinctive hooked beak—a characteristic that enhances its dignified and somewhat fierce mien—provides it with a very effective instrument for tearing and killing. It also has short, powerful legs and prehensile claws that enable it to take a firm, almost unbreakable grip on its struggling victim. The talons too are quite strong, and are bent and pointed, with sharp edges.

Together with the kite and the hawk, the eagle is classified among a relatively small family of diurnal birds of prey (hunters by day), although formerly it was grouped with the falcons. Another day-hunter, the vulture, is a member of the same

CLASSIFICATION. *Aquila chrysaëtos* (golden eagle) and *Aquila heliaca* (imperial eagle), members of Buteoninae subfamily of Accipitridae family of order Falconiformes.

LEXICON. *Hebrew:* NESHER, NESHAR. *Greek:* AETOS.

family, and all of these birds are members of the same zoological order. Of them all, the eagle and the vulture attain the largest size.

CONFUSED WITH VULTURE

As often happens with the fauna of the Old Testament, especially the birds, there is some confusion about the exact meaning of the Hebrew word. In the case of the eagle, *nesher* unquestionably does mean "eagle," but there are certain passages where, in the opinion of some translators, it also could mean "vulture." For example, in the book of Proverbs appears the statement: "The eye that mocks a father and scorns to obey a mother will be picked out by the ravens . . . and eaten by the vultures" (Prov. 30:17). The Hebrew word used here is *nesher*, but it is translated "vulture," for the vulture is much better known as a carrion-eater—often going first to the eyes of the corpse—whereas the eagle seldom feeds on dead creatures. In the Mosaic dietary laws the eagle is specifically forbidden (Lev. 11:13; Deut. 14:12), along with the vulture and several other birds of prey.

GOLDEN AND IMPERIAL EAGLES

The golden eagle is one of the most powerful of all eagles, and, along with the imperial eagle, was probably the most common variety living in Palestine in ancient times. It is just under three feet long with a wing span of six feet or more, although the male is somewhat smaller, a phenomenon applying to all diurnal birds of prey. Male and female usually hunt together, from shortly after sunrise until about noon. Circling in a majestic gliding flight far above the ground, they are an imposing sight. When the sharp-eyed eagle discovers what might be prey, it begins a spiraling descent to make a closer inspection. Suddenly it folds its wings and plunges down upon some unfortunate animal at top speed, at the last moment extending its claws and sinking them into the victim with a

139

grip so sure that seldom has the animal a chance to escape.

For Jeremiah and other prophets, the great speed and sureness of the eagle were the epitome of swiftness; the fearful war horses of the Scythians, as they come up against Israel, are thus described as "swifter than eagles" (Jer. 4:13; cf. Hab. 1:8). And the Pentateuch employs a similar comparison to emphasize the sudden striking power of a hostile army: "The Lord will bring a nation against you from afar . . . as swift as the eagle flies" (Deut. 28:49). The high altitude at which an eagle soars was noticed and applied to a human situation by one of the proverbists: "Do not toil to acquire wealth; be wise enough to desist. When your eyes light upon it, it is gone; for suddenly it takes to itself wings, flying like an eagle toward heaven" (Prov. 23:4-5; cf. Rev. 12:14).

SYMBOL OF ENEMY

The eagle's strength and invincibility are often mentioned in the Bible, particularly with reference to a powerful and hostile nation that is attacking Israel. The prophet Ezekiel describes King Nebuchadnezzar in these picturesque words: "A great eagle with great wings and long pinions, rich in plumage of many colors, came to Lebanon and took the top of the cedar" (Ezek. 17:3). Nebuchadnezzar's subjects, the Babylonians, as well as their predecessors in the shifting domination of the ancient Near East, the Assyrians, frequently depicted the eagle in their art, especially as a deity with the body of a man and the head of an eagle. But in the book of Daniel, Nebuchadnezzar himself has an experience which made him almost the real-life counterpart of the imaginary

Among the ancient Assyrians the eagle was held in such high regard that it was depicted as a deity; here a half-man, half-eagle is shown on a wall panel from the palace of a ninth century B.C. king, pollinating a "sacred tree." (Photograph courtesy of the Metropolitan Museum of Art; gift of John D. Rockefeller, Jr., 1932.)

eagle-man. Deposed from his throne and banished, in a demented state of mind, to the wilderness, "his hair grew as long as eagles' feathers, and his nails were like birds' claws" (Dan. 4:33), and he lived in this condition for many years.

INACCESSIBLE NEST

The eagle builds its nest on inaccessible mountain peaks or at the top of the tallest trees, a fact noted by Jeremiah, who contrasts the safety of the eagle in its eyrie with the state of the sinful man who cannot escape God: "Though you make your nest as high as the eagle's, I will bring you down from there, says the Lord" (Jer. 49:16; cf. Obad. 4). Hatched in the sanctity of the eagle's nest is a brood consisting of two, and occasionally three, eggs. Only the female sits on the nest, but the young eaglets are fed by both parents, who are greatly devoted to their offspring and train them with great care in the difficult art of flying. Something of this devotion is referred to when the Lord says to the people of Israel, concerning the Exodus: "You have seen what I did to the Egyptians, and how I bore you on eagle's wings and brought you to myself" (Exod. 19:4; cf. Deut. 32:11). The eagle can attain a very old age. There are cases of eagles in captivity that have lived to an age of more than a hundred years. No wonder then that a Hebrew poet implies that this bird has discovered some sort of "fountain of youth" when he says: "Bless the Lord, O my soul, . . . who satisfies you with good as long as you live so that your youth is renewed like the eagle's" (Ps. 103:1, 5).

The mien and behavior of the eagle often struck the biblical authors with awe and wonder, as they still do us today, and one of the proverbists (Agur of Massa) sums up these feelings perhaps for all time: "Three things are too wonderful for me; four I do not understand: the way of an eagle in the sky, the way of a serpent on a rock, the way of a ship on the high seas, and the way of a man with a maiden" (Prov. 30:18-19).

Falcon   Hawk   Kite

Mentioned in the Bible among the birds prohibited as food, the falcon, the kite, and the hawk are, like the eagle, diurnal birds of prey and all belong to the same zoological order. In the Mosaic dietary laws each is prohibited "according to its kind" (Lev. 11:13-16; Deut. 14:12-16), revealing that even in ancient times many species of these birds existed in Palestine.

One of the smaller falcons often seen today in Palestine is the common kestrel. Despite its size, it is, like all falcons, an excellent flyer; a special characteristic of its flight is the way it stops from time to time to hover in mid-air on extended wings, a trait that has given it the name "wind-hover." The

---

CLASSIFICATION. *Falco tinnunculus* (kestrel), member of subfamily Polihieracinae; *Falco peregrinus* (peregrine falcon), member of subfamily Falconinae; both members of Falconidae family of order Falconiformes. *Milvus milvus* (common red kite) and *Accipiter nisus* (sparrow hawk), both members of subfamily Accipitrinae; *Buteo ferox* (long-legged buzzard), member of subfamily Buteoninae; all three members of Accipitridae family of order Falconiformes.

LEXICON. Falcon—*Hebrew:* AYYAH. Kite—*Hebrew:* DAYYAH. Hawk—*Hebrew:* NETS. Buzzard—*Hebrew:* RAAH.

The Egyptians, among other ancient Near Eastern peoples, were particularly fond of the falcon (above), which bore religious significance in their art. This bird, with stiffly stylized wings, appeared as an inlay on a wooden shrine of the Late Dynastic period (500-350 B.C.). (Photograph courtesy of the Metropolitan Museum of Art. From the Carnarvon Collection; gift of Edward S. Harkness, 1926.)

The hawk (right) represented Horus, the god of day, to the Egyptians. This painted "hawk box" comes from a tomb of the Ptolemaic period, only a century or two before the birth of Christ. (Photograph courtesy of the Metropolitan Museum of Art; Rogers Fund, 1912.)

kestrel's wings are long and pointed, and its long tail is rounded off at the end. It feeds primarily on insects, small rodents, occasionally on small birds, and often appears in flocks of ten to twelve pairs. Another variety of falcon common to Palestine is the peregrine falcon, so named because it is found all over the world. This is the species that is chiefly used in the sport of falconry (although hawks, and even eagles, are also trained for this purpose).

In the Old Testament the falcon is mentioned only once outside of the book of Leviticus (it is omitted in the Deuteronomy dietary laws), and that is in the book of Job. There we are told: "That path [to the interior of the earth, where the miners work] no bird of prey knows, and the falcon's eye

has not seen it" (Job 28:7). This saying is simply a poetic way of expressing the truism that man has available to him treasures that are denied to other creatures of the earth.

FORBIDDEN BIRDS OF PREY

The kite, forbidden in both sets of dietary laws, is easily distinguished by its long, forked tail. It is a migratory bird known to stay in Palestine during the summer, especially in the mountains of southern Judea, in the trackless wastes west of the Dead Sea, and in the wilderness of Beersheba. As the scavenger of the hawk family (actually subfamily), it is logically associated with places deserted by human beings: "Thorns shall grow over its [Edom's] strongholds, nettles and thistles in its fortresses. . . . There shall the kites be gathered, each one with her mate" (Isa. 34:13, 15). Here again, however, as with the eagle, the reference may be to a species of vulture (so translated in the KJV).

Of the several hawks found in Palestine, the most common is—and was probably in biblical times—the sparrow hawk, a relatively small bird of prey that prefers to build its nest in tall trees. It too is mentioned only once outside of the dietary laws—in the book of Job, where its migratory trait is alluded to: "Is it by your wisdom that the hawk soars, and spreads his wings toward the south?" (Job 39:26). God is speaking here, enumerating to Job the wonders of nature, the divine creation.

The buzzard should also be mentioned, since its name is used in the RSV. It resembles the hawk, but is more closely related to eagles and vultures. It is a large, powerful bird with broad, rounded wings and a fan-shaped tail. The long-legged buzzard, somewhat larger than the common buzzard, is found in Palestine and also in the western parts of Asia and in Syria. There is some doubt about the textual accuracy of the Hebrew word *raah*, which appears only in Deuteronomy 14 and is translated "buzzard" in the RSV.

The Goose

Although never mentioned specifically by name in the Bible, the goose was undoubtedly known in biblical times, and the "fatted fowl" that appeared on the lavish table of King Solomon and were a daily requirement of the royal kitchen were probably geese (I Kings 4:23). There is no other biblical reference of the same sort, but the many depictions of this succulent fowl in Near Eastern art lead us to believe that it was well known to the Hebrews.

Geese form a large and distinct subfamily (Anserinae) within the zoological family that also includes ducks and swans, and are distributed all over the world. There are many different species, subspecies, and breeds, and it is of course impossible to specify which is referred to in I Kings. Even though geese are aquatic birds with webbed feet and "waterproof" feathers, many varieties spend most of their lives on

---

CLASSIFICATION. Geese belong to the subfamily Anserinae of Anatidae family of order Anseriformes. *Alopochen aegypticus* (Nile goose), member of Anatinae subfamily (ducks) of Anatidae family of order Anseriformes.

LEXICON. *Hebrew:* BARBURIM.

Even as early at 2500 B.C. the goose was apparently considered
a delicacy in Egypt, as this relief carving of tribute bearers,
fashioned of limestone for an ancient tomb, testifies. (Photograph courtesy of the Metropolitan Museum of Art; Rogers
Fund, 1908.)

land, and some even build their nests in trees. On the whole, wild geese tend to be found in flatlands and prairies rather than in mountainous terrain.

"SILLY GOOSE"

A relatively intelligent, cautious, and alert bird, the goose has for some reason gained a reputation for stupidity, as expressed in the common phrase "silly goose." But when a flight of geese lands to rest, several geese are posted at once as guards to warn against the approach of any danger. Always suspicious of human beings, the goose can nevertheless distinguish hunters from farmers and shepherds. In captivity it is quickly tamed and, apart from a certain tendency to be demanding and quarrelsome, can be an intelligent, attractive pet. After the mating contest between male geese, or ganders, which can be quite violent, geese conduct an admirable life of domestic tranquillity. The mated geese remain together for the rest of their lives, faithful and devoted to one another, living peaceably with their neighboring "families." The female hatches her eggs alone, while the gander is the "man of the house," the watchman and fearless defender.

NILE GOOSE

The Nile (or Egyptian) goose is often featured in Egyptian wall paintings from ancient times. (In spite of its gooselike appearance, this species is now considered to be biologically closer to ducks than to true geese.) A pretty, varicolored bird with a purple beak and red feet, it occurs today in northern Africa, Palestine, and Syria. Equally at home on land or in the water, it runs, swims, dives, and flies with great skill. The young Nile goose is especially fond of locusts and grasshoppers, a fact which endears it to farmers. Large flocks of these brightly colored fowl can be seen today for many miles along the banks of the upper Nile, especially in the wooded areas, where they often build their nests in trees.

The Heron

The word "heron" actually denotes an entire suborder of birds that includes bitterns and egrets, but ordinarily we think of the heron as a bird that possesses considerably more physical beauty than the bittern (q.v.). Our image is of a long-legged, long-necked bird, with a crested head, standing in stately solitude in a shallow creek or marsh. There are some sixty species of this kind of heron (composing the Ardeidae family), distributed throughout almost the entire world.

One of the most common species, the blue-gray heron, winters in southern Europe and North Africa, migrating to northern Europe in the early spring. In Palestine it builds its winter nest near water—in swamps and along river banks—

CLASSIFICATION. *Ardea cinerea* (blue-gray heron), *Casmerodius albus* (greater egret), *Nycticorax nycticorax* (black-crowned night heron), all members of the Ardeidae family of suborder Ardeae of order Ciconiiformes (long-legged wading birds).

LEXICON. *Hebrew:* ANAPHAH.

for it lives on fish and frogs. It will stand patiently in the water for hours; then, suddenly, the long, pointed beak darts down with lightning speed to catch the prey. Often the blue-gray heron builds its nest in a tall tree, to which it may return year after year. Since the heron is actually a gregarious bird,

This Egyptian wall painting, executed during the period of the Exodus (Nineteenth Dynasty, 1320-1200 B.C.), gives us a remarkably accurate depiction of a heron, readily recognizable as the common blue-gray species. (Photograph courtesy of the Oriental Institute of the University of Chicago. From Davies, *Ancient Egyptian Paintings.*)

one often finds many such nests close to one another, in colonies called "heronries."

GREATER EGRET

There are other varieties of heron in Palestine, among them the beautiful greater egret (also called the "common egret" or "great white heron"), which lives in the swamps on the coastal plain of Syria. A snow white coat of feathers gives this bird its characteristic appearance. The feathers of its crest—like the shining, metallic-gray neck feathers of the blue-gray heron—are coveted as decoration for hats. In some areas of the Near East these birds were hunted almost to extinction. In former times hunting falcons were employed in this sport, although often they were no match for the heron's long beak. Also found in Palestine is the black-crowned night heron, so called because of the markings along its back and on the crown of its head and because it is active mostly during the night. Like the blue-gray heron, it builds its nests in trees. It is differentiated from other herons by its thicker beak and shorter legs.

ALL SPECIES FORBIDDEN

Herons are mentioned only twice in the Bible, and it should come as no surprise that the references appear in the two sets of dietary laws in the Pentateuch, where there is so much detail in the enumeration of all the unclean birds, animals, snakes, and insects. The Mosaic law, recognizing that there are several kinds of heron available to the Israelites, makes no exception among them: "The heron according to its kind," that is, all species of heron are forbidden as food for the Israelites (Lev. 11:19; Deut. 14:18).

The Ostrich

The ostrich, that strange bird most of us see only in zoos or motion pictures, was at one time much more widely distributed than it is today. Nowadays the North African variety is found only in the area from the Atlas Mountains to the Sudan, but at one time another variety existed in large numbers throughout Arabia and, presumably, as far north as Syria. In antiquity it was probably to be found in the highlands east of the Jordan River, where the Israelites encountered it.

The largest of all extant birds, a fully grown ostrich may stand eight feet tall and measure some six feet from the beak to the tip of the tail, and may weigh as much as three hundred pounds. The body is thickset and strong, and the thighs are almost as heavy as those of a man. Its long, powerful legs are covered with scales, and its feet have two toes each, a feature that is unique to the ostrich among the larger, flight-

---

CLASSIFICATION. *Struthio camelus*, member of Struthionidae family of order Struthioniformes.

LEXICON. *Hebrew:* BATH YAANAH, RENANIM (?).

In this wax impression from a cylindrical stone seal is depicted an ostrich hunt. The artist was obviously more interested in extolling the prowess of the hunter than in accuracy, since it is virtually impossible to catch this bird on foot. The seal is from the Middle Assyrian period (1400-1000 B.C.). (Photograph courtesy of the Pierpont Morgan Library.)

less birds. Its neck is long and bare, and its head is small and flat, with large eyes and long "feminine" lashes that protrude from the upper lids.

NO EASY CATCH

Although it cannot fly (lacking "flight feathers" that resist the air), the ostrich uses its wings to good effect in running, when it spreads out its long tail feathers like a sail and seems to "row" the air with its wings. The soft, downlike tail feathers of the ostrich have been much prized by humans at various times in the past for ornamental use—most recently in the 1920's for women's hats. Especially popular have been the shining white feathers of the male, who during the mating season presents a stunning appearance, his body adorned with coal-black and snow-white feathers and his legs and neck glowing with a bright red.

Thus ostriches have been hunted through the ages—biblical times not excepted. But the ostrich is no easy catch, for with its long stride it can run at speeds of up to forty miles an hour. The author of Job recognized its swiftness when he said of the ostrich: "When she rouses herself to flee, she laughs at the horse and his rider" (Job 39:18). And, in fact, horses that are to be used in hunting these birds must undergo a long and careful training.

BELLOWING OSTRICH

Another distinctive feature of the ostrich is its strange cry, which the male utters when danger approaches or at night: it is a wailing sound resembling the bellow of a suffering ox. Undoubtedly it is this sound that the prophet has in mind in his description of his own sorrow over the punishment that the Lord will allow to ravage Samaria and Jerusalem: "For this I will lament and wail; I will go stripped and naked; I will make lamentation like the jackals, and mourning like the ostriches" (Mic. 1:8).

155

The female digs her nest in the sand, where she lays up to twenty-five eggs at a time, of which she is able to hatch only about fifteen; the rest become food for the newly hatched birds, for wandering jackals, and even for human beings, for the yolk is quite palatable. The largest of all birds' eggs, naturally enough, an ostrich egg is about six inches long and rounded off at both ends, with an extremely hard, yellowish-white shell. Each one weighs as much as two dozen hens' eggs, or about three and a half pounds. Male and female alternate hatching the eggs, the male taking over at night because of his darker coloring, while the female, whose color blends into that of the desert sand, broods during the day. Occasionally the female leaves the nest during the middle of the day and covers the eggs with sand, allowing the sun to do the hatching, and this trait too is noted by the author of Job: "The wings of the ostrich wave proudly; but are they the pinions and plumage of love? For she leaves her eggs to the earth, and lets them be warmed on the ground" (Job 39:13-14).

NOT SO FOOLISH

Also in Job is the statement that "God has made her [the ostrich] forget wisdom" (Job 39:17), which is in accord with an Arab proverb that refers to the "foolish ostrich." This proverbial stupidity probably has something to do with the way that a running ostrich sticks to a chosen path from which it will not deviate, enabling a clever hunter to ambush it easily. But the common adage about "burying one's head in the sand like an ostrich," implying that the ostrich believes that it cannot be seen when it can see nothing, has no basis in fact. When it is alerted, the bird will lay its head flat on the ground, peering at whatever is causing the disturbance— an act which, when viewed from a distance, appears to be a burying of the head in the sand.

The preference of the ostrich for living in solitary, deserted places is affirmed by Isaiah's description of the destruction of Babylon: "Its houses will be full of howling creatures; there ostriches will dwell" (Isa. 13:21; cf. Jer. 50:39). Isaiah uses a similar picture to describe the punishment of Edom: "Thorns shall grow over its strongholds, nettles and thistles in its fortresses. It shall be the haunt of jackals, an abode for ostriches" (Isa. 34:13). Jackals and ostriches are often mentioned together by the prophetic writers to create a feeling of desolation or to picture a wild place, as in the Lord's promise to Israel: "I will make a way in the wilderness and rivers in the desert. The wild beasts will honor me, the jackals and the ostriches" (Isa. 43:19-20).

"DAUGHTER OF GREEDINESS"

The reference in Lamentations to "the ostriches in the wilderness" (Lam. 4:3) is one of those passages in which the exact translation is not certain. Several literal translations have been suggested, all of them pointing to some trait of the ostrich: "the daughter of the wilderness"; or, "the daughter of the cry," referring to the peculiar call of the ostrich mentioned above; or, again, as "the daughter of greediness," bringing to mind another characteristic of the ostrich. It will eat almost anything—without seeming to care. Odd objects have been found in the stomachs of ostriches, including even entirely indigestible rocks and pieces of metal.

BANNED

Perhaps it is this greediness, the huge and indiscriminate appetite of the ostrich, that led to the ban on using it for food among the Israelites. The Mosaic law declares: "And these you shall have in abomination among the birds, they shall not be eaten, they are an abomination: . . . the ostrich . . ." (Lev. 11:13, 16; Deut. 14:15). Ostrich meat, however, has always been a favorite food among the Arabs, and Westerners too have found it quite delicious.

157

The Owl

Through the ages superstitious people have been fascinated by the owl—and who does not become a bit superstitious when, traveling through a lonely spot on a dark night, he hears the hoot of the owl? Now a soft and melancholy plaint, now a high, shrill screech, it alarms even the most skeptical and brave. Since almost all varieties are nocturnal, one rarely sees an owl by day—or, for that matter, by night. It is quite impossible to hear the owl when it is in flight, for its wing and tail feathers are soft as velvet. It only reveals its presence by its unearthly call.

It is as a bearer of misfortune and an omen of disaster that the owl most often makes its appearance in the Old Testa-

---

CLASSIFICATION. *Athene noctua* (little owl), *Asio otus* (long-eared owl), *Otus scops* (screech or scops owl), all members of Strigidae family (typical owls); *Tyto alba* (common barn owl), *Tyto aluca* (tawny owl), both members of Tytonidae family (barn owls); both families of order Strigiformes.

LEXICON. *Hebrew:* YANSHUPH, KOS, QIPPOZ, LILITH, TACHMAS (?), TINSHEMETH (?).

ment. "I am like . . . an owl of the waste places" (Ps. 102:6), says one Hebrew poet in describing his sufferings: he is shunned, taunted, and derided by his fellows, for no one will associate with someone who is a harbinger of death. In Isaiah's graphic description of the destruction of Edom, the sinister mood is heightened by a reference to the owl: "From generation to generation it shall lie waste; . . . the owl and the raven shall dwell in it" (Isa. 34:10-11). Compare this passage with Zeph. 2:14: "The owl shall hoot in the window"; actually the Hebrew word used in Zephaniah refers only to a "voice," but the RSV translator has taken the liberty of placing the owl in a context where it certainly is appropriate. These passages show, too, that the owl has not changed its mode of living. They can still be found in the temple ruins and pyramids of Egypt, and in rock-hewn graves, ruins, and caves, on both sides of the Jordan. They seldom come near dwellings that are still inhabited.

OWL'S "FACE"

Owls actually comprise an entire order of birds of prey, and all but a few species are nocturnal. They once were considered part of the Falconiformes (eagles, hawks, and vultures), but they possess some unique physical traits. For example, the owl is the only bird whose eyes are turned forward. Since these eyes are surrounded by circles of small stiff feathers, the owl gives the impression of having a "face," and in some species almost a "monkey face." The owl's sight and hearing are highly developed. Its unusually large eyes are almost useless, however, in the daylight, for light dazzles them. Despite appearances, the owl actually has a rather small and slender body, about the size of a pigeon's; its bulkiness comes from the thick heavy layer of feathers that covers its body. It feeds on all kinds of small creatures such as mice, voles, shrews, and small birds. These it swallows whole, for its esophagus is quite elastic. Later it disgorges the inedible

159

The "face" of the owl is easily discernible in this detail from a stone relief found in an Egyptian tomb. Actually the figure here is a hieroglyph and forms part of a written inscription. (Photograph courtesy of the University Museum, Philadelphia.)

parts—fur, feathers, bones—in the form of "owl pellets," which one may find in woods where owls nest.

There are about two hundred species of owls, distributed over the entire earth (including the Arctic), and several are found in Palestine. The problem of identifying the owls of the Old Testament is a formidable one: a number of Hebrew words are used, apparently to denote the various species, but it is not even certain that all of these words definitely refer to owls. As a result English translations of the Bible vary from passage to passage, mentioning everything from the ibis to the swan.

The most common owl in Palestine is the species known as the "little owl," a descendant, apparently, of the owl usually pictured with the Greek goddess Pallas Athene. Probably this owl is the one called *kos* in Hebrew, which is always translated as "owl" or "little owl" in our Bibles. Another Hebrew word for owl is *yanshuph,* which we may take to mean the long-eared owl, a woodland variety named for the large erect tufts at the sides of its head. In the KJV it is called the "great owl," and in the RSV it is called the "ibis" or the "great owl" (Lev. 11:17; Deut. 14:16). Both versions translate it as "owl" in Isa. 34:11. The barn owl is also found in Palestine, and the best guess is that it appears in the Bible under the name *tinshemeth.* But our Bibles translate this word as "water hen" (RSV) or "swan" (KJV) in two places in the dietary laws (Lev. 11:18; Deut. 14:16), and as "chameleon" (RSV) or "mole" (KJV) in another place (Lev. 11:30). Another bird mentioned in the dietary laws, *tachmas* in Hebrew, is also believed by some to be the barn owl; however, it is translated as "nighthawk" (or "hawk") in our Bibles, and there is much support for this interpretation. The nighthawk is not a hawk at all, but a nightjar, sometimes called the goatsucker. Some interpreters also believe that *tinshemeth* refers to the nightjar. (See the Appendix.) The barn owl, a handsome, slim bird with delicately marked plumage, builds its nests near human dwellings. In the Near East there is a superstition that it flies through open windows to scratch the faces of sleeping children.

TAWNY OWL

Aside from the owl mentioned in Psalm 102, which is *qippoz* in Hebrew and may be the screech (or scops) owl, the only other reference to an owl occurs in Isa. 34:14. In his description of the judgment of the nations, the prophet declares: "Yea, there shall the night hag alight, and find for herself a resting place." The Hebrew word translated here as "night hag" ("screech owl" in the KJV) is *lilith,* which may denote a very common owl in Palestine, the tawny owl. In any case, it is almost definitely some sort of owl and not a "night hag."

The Partridge

The game bird known as the partridge is represented by several species in Palestine, which are to be found throughout the mountainous regions of Judea, the lower section of the Jordan Valley, and in the vicinity of the Dead Sea. The most common partridge in the area is the chukar, varieties of which are found as far east as India (whence comes its name). Resembling the common French partridge of Europe, its body is about sixteen inches long and is covered with beautiful and radiantly colored feathers. The Hebrew name for the partridge, *qore*, means literally "the crier." Behind this name is, perhaps, the observation that at eventide the male birds run through the fields calling the scattered hens.

PARTRIDGE HUNTING

The partridge is a very agile bird on the ground, capable of running exceptionally fast to escape its pursuers. But it does not have exceptional stamina, and so, when the Arabs hunt these birds they simply run them until the partridges are com-

---

CLASSIFICATION. *Alectoris graeca werae* (chukar partridge), member of subfamily Phasianinae (quails, partridges, pheasants) of Phasianidae family of order Galliformes (fowl).

LEXICON. *Hebrew:* QORE.

Hunters can catch this chukar partridge, the most common species in Palestine, in their bare hands, after running the bird to exhaustion. (Photograph courtesy of the Free Library of Philadelphia.)

pletely exhausted. The hunters can then either catch them in their bare hands or kill them by beating them with sticks. This method was undoubtedly known in biblical times, for when David was running away from Saul in the mountains of Judea he compared his own plight to that of the partridge: "The king of Israel has come out to seek my life, like one who hunts a partridge in the mountains" (I Sam. 26:20). As in the case of the partridge, David's fast legs were his only defense against Saul; but unlike many of these birds, he did manage to escape.

The mating season for the partridge is in the spring, and following this time the male and female stay together as a family. The female begins to lay eggs in May, but the hatching does not start until two months later. The nest, which is only a small depression in the earth scantily lined with vegetation, is often located close to a well-traveled thoroughfare. When the chicks emerge from the eggs they are so well developed that they can leave the nest immediately, and after two or three weeks they are able to take care of themselves.

NOT DUPED

The only mention of the partridge outside of I Samuel occurs in the book of Jeremiah, where the prophet declares: "Like a partridge hatching eggs which she has not laid, is the man who amasses wealth which he has not justly earned; in the midst of his days he must leave it, and at the end he will prove himself a fool" (Jer. 17:11, *An American Translation*, J. M. Powis Smith and Edgar J. Goodspeed; this version is the clearest rendering of a rather obscure passage). There is a popular but erroneous belief that the partridge is in the habit of unknowingly hatching other birds' eggs. It is true that generally a bird is unable to judge whether the eggs it hatches are its own or some other's, and most of us have read how the cowbird, among others, takes advantage of other birds in this respect. The belief that the partridge is always being duped, however, probably arises from the fact that the hen lays two batches of eggs (a total of about twenty), one of which it hatches itself and the other of which is hatched by the male.

The Peacock

The peacock is actually the male peafowl, whose mate is properly known as the peahen. However, when we think of this bird we think of the male, who is the real "celebrity" of the family. He is the one who attracts attention because of his decorative appearance and who has, throughout history, been kept in captivity in everything from royal courts to city zoos. The best known species is native to India and Ceylon, and there is also a Javan variety. Thus the peacock, which is really closely related to the common pheasant, has always been associated with the "mysterious East."

What gives the peacock his stately, luxurious appearance is his magnificent feathers, especially the metallic, gleaming, resplendently colored breast and tail feathers. Situated above the regular tail feathers is a covert of feathers that are unusually elongated and trail along behind the peacock on the

---

CLASSIFICATION. *Pavo cristatus* (common peafowl), member of subfamily Phasianinae (quails, partridges, pheasants) of Phasianidae family of order Galliformes (fowl).

LEXICON. *Hebrew:* TUKKIYYIM.

In sancti thome apli. Jr p
nus vis. ad migt. ꝶ in ma
tutinis ad bñd. aã. Oua vi
disti me thoma ardidisti beati
qui non viderunt et ardiderut
alleluya. Oratio.
Da nobis qs dñe
beati apli tui tho
me sollennitatibz gliari.
ut eius semp ꝶ patrocinus
subleuemur. ꝶ fidem con
gnia deuotione sectemur
Per dñm. lc. pña.
Thomas hebraice la
tine abissus vel gminus i
terptatur. ꝶ grece didimus
nominatur. vtraqz enim
interptatio eius statui con
gruit. Didimus ꝶ te vo
cari potuit propter dubii

cor in credendo effcatu dñice
resurrectionis. Abissus q
altitudine diuice virtuti
in resurrectione certa fide
pnetrauit. Et inirta lati
nam lingua xpi genuin
ac similis saluatori aut
endo incredulus videns
fidelis. Icio seda.
Hic euangeliu pdi
cauit parthis medis psi
thicauis qz bragmanis
et destinatus ad orienta
plagam mitia gentium
penetrans. ibiqz pdicat
onem suam vsqz ad vli
mui sue passionis pduce
xpcatus est ad indiani sit
proiem p riuelatione. E
ad opinione eius omnie
pli festinabant videntes
signa ꝶ prodigia magna
que faciebat. ꝶ non poter
contempnere predicatio
eius. Pdo tent.
Nam ꝶ demones pe
lebat ꝶ cecos illuminabat
onis dolores ꝶ calores ꝶ
gores tollebat. ꝶ etiam r
tuos suscitabat. Cuius
pus cum honore ꝶ hymn
transtulerunt ad ecclia

ground, giving him an overall length of up to six feet. The feathers of the covert can be raised to form a huge fan, revealing that the tip of each is adorned with a multicolored "eye." The feathers are raised during courtship, when the peacock makes them vibrate and give off a distinct rustling noise. The peahen, however, is rather drab and lacks the long covert.

IMPORTED PEACOCKS

In biblical times the peacock was imported by the Near Eastern countries. According to the Old Testament the beauty-loving King Solomon had "ships of Tarshish" (a Phoenician colony in Spain, after which large merchant vessels were named) at sea, and "once every three years the fleet of ships of Tarshish used to come bringing gold, silver, ivory, apes, and peacocks" (I Kings 10:22; II Chron. 9:21). There is some doubt, however, that the Hebrew word used here is properly translated as "peacocks," and some interpreters take it to mean some kind of monkey. There is evidence, however, that the Phoenicians—the "world travelers" of the time—did introduce the bird to the Pharaohs of Egypt, perhaps as early as the time of Solomon.

In the early Christian church the peacock became a symbol of immortality, promised in the resurrection of Christ. In addition, the "eyes" of its tail came to represent the "all-seeing eyes" of the church.

Representing the life everlasting that Christ brings to his followers, these peacocks adorn an early sixteenth-century Latin breviary. The illuminator has caught them in various poses—standing, perching, and with covert erect. (Photograph courtesy of the Pierpont Morgan Library.)

The Pelican

One of the more curious-looking birds that inhabit the earth is the pelican. Largest of all the aquatic birds, considerably larger than even the swan, it is well known for its pouch—actually an elastic fold of skin—with which its long beak is equipped. The upper part of the sixteen-inch beak is hooked downward at the end, and all in all it is an ideal contrivance for catching fish—which the pelican does, and with a prodigious appetite.

Pelicans belong to a fairly small order which is named after them (Pelecaniformes). There are ten species of pelicans and the one that may have been known to biblical writers is called the common pelican. The adult of this species is white with a faint rose tinge, and has black feathers growing from the wing-joint farthest from the body; the legs, the pouch, and the skin around the eyes are yellow, while the hook of the beak is red. The common pelican may grow to be six feet long, with a wingspan of up to eight feet. The female lays

CLASSIFICATION. *Pelecanus onocrotalus* (common pelican), member of Pelecanidae family of order Pelecaniformes.
LEXICON. *Hebrew:* QAATH.

168

two or three eggs at a time, and about four weeks later the grayish-brown young birds are hatched.

While most birds feed their young by putting food into their mouths, the pelican reverses the process: the young pelican sticks its head and most of its body into its mother's throat and plucks food from the mother's crop. When the young are to be fed, the mother props open her jaws so far that the lower beak rests against her breast. Because the food in the mother's crop consists of crushed and bloody raw fish, the idea developed in ancient times that the pelican feeds its young with blood drawn from its own breast. By virtue of this old superstition the pelican came to be a symbol of mercy in ancient Christian art.

There is some question as to whether pelicans are actually mentioned in the Bible, and the Hebrew word *qaath* is trans-

Dating from the Eighteenth Dynasty (fourteenth century B.C.), this Egyptian wall painting gives an accurate depiction of a group of pelicans. Note their size in relation to the kneeling slave. (Photograph courtesy of the Oriental Institute of the University of Chicago.)

lated as "pelican" in the RSV only in the dietary laws (Lev. 11:18; Deut. 14:17). Like all the other birds listed by name in these sections, they are pronounced unclean. Although pelicans are occasionally seen today along the Jordan, the Sea of Galilee, and Lake Hule, where they build their nests among the dense rush thickets, some interpreters believe that *qaath* means "night bird," and thus refers to either an owl (q.v.) or a nightjar (see the Appendix). Except in the dietary laws, the RSV chooses to call it a hawk or a vulture, while the KJV is more consistent, staying with the pelican or, on two occasions, the closely related cormorant. In any case, this bird is pictured by biblical writers as a part of a scene of desolation, where human life has come to an end.

PELICAN OF THE WILDERNESS

"I am like a pelican of the wilderness: I am like an owl of the desert" (Ps. 102:6, KJV), says one of the Hebrew poets, and if the pelican is meant here, the "wilderness" refers simply to the swamps and unpopulated river banks favored by the pelican, or any deserted place. When Zephaniah speaks of the impending destruction of Nineveh, a city located near the Tigris, he uses the following words: "Both the cormorant [pelican] and the bittern shall lodge in the upper lintels of it" (Zeph. 2:14, KJV); a pelican often seeks out a tree or some other high and inaccessible place in which to sleep. The one other biblical reference to this bird is found in Isaiah's description of the Lord's judgment upon Edom: "But the cormorant [pelican] and the bittern shall possess it; . . . and he shall stretch out upon it the line of confusion, and the stones of emptiness" (Isa. 34:11, KJV).

The Quail

Wherever the quail is mentioned in the Bible, it is as food—which is not surprising, for it is considered by many gourmets to be the most delicious of the game birds. Closely related to partridges (q.v.) and pheasants, the quail is considerably smaller than either, reaching a length of only about eight inches. Five species are known; they are distributed throughout the Old World and also are found in Australia. The species which was probably known to the Israelites is the common quail, a reddish-brown bird with dark brown markings and buff underparts. Quails generally feed on weed seeds and insects, and thus are welcomed by farmers.

A peculiarity of this bird is its migratory habits, which are not nearly as regular as those of other birds of passage. A flock of quails that has been breeding on the fertile plains of southern Europe will not depart for the south en masse; instead, some begin their flight as early as August, while others

---

CLASSIFICATION. *Coturnix coturnix* (the common quail), member of subfamily Phasianinae (quails, partridges, pheasants) of Phasianidae family of order Galliformes (fowl).

LEXICON. *Hebrew:* SELAV.

A plump, rather timorous quail sits in the midst of foliage in this woven tapestry from the Coptic church of Egypt in the third or fourth century A.D. (Photograph courtesy of the Metropolitan Museum of Art; gift of George F. Baker, 1890.)

wait another month or two before leaving. In addition, the quail is not very adept at flying. It has trouble covering long distances at one stretch, and yet it migrates a considerable distance, flying from Europe to the tropical regions of Africa and back each year. To make up for its deficiencies, it flies mostly during the night and tries to make use of favorable winds.

In the course of both their spring and fall migrations, quails arrive in Egypt and Arabia so exhausted that they can be caught with the bare hands as they alight. Thousands of them are thus caught, even by children, and are killed, impaled on sticks, and sold in the market places. In some areas those that are not eaten immediately are beheaded, plucked, and eviscerated, after which they are split, salted, smoked, and packed like herring for shipment and sale. Since catching quail is easy and has become profitable, some consideration is being given to the possibility of instituting protective legislation to prevent them from becoming extinct.

COVERED THE CAMP

The quail is mentioned in two similar stories taking place during the Israelites' exodus from Egypt. The first occurs in the second month of their sojourn: the Israelites had already become dissatisfied with their scanty wilderness diet and the hardships of their nomadic existence. They longed for the fleshpots of Egypt, even though they had lived there as slaves. Then the Lord said to them: "At twilight you shall eat flesh." And "in the evening quails came up and covered the camp" (Exod. 16:12-13). The second account, in the book of Numbers, offers more detail and leaves no room for doubt that the bird mentioned here is the quail. Once again the Israelites were murmuring against the Lord and demanding meat to eat. Moses accepted their demand and presented it to the Lord, who lost patience with his Chosen People and declared that they would get their meat, for "a whole month, until it comes out at your nostrils and becomes loathsome to you, because you have rejected the Lord who is among you, and have wept before him, saying, 'Why did we come forth out of Egypt?'" (Num. 11:20).

STILL HAPPENS

And thus it happened: "There went forth a wind from the Lord, and it brought quails from the sea, and let them fall beside the camp, about a day's journey on this side and a day's journey on the other side, round about the camp, and about two cubits deep on the face of the earth. And the people rose all that day, and all night, and all the next day, and gathered the quails; he who gathered least gathered ten homers; and they spread them out for themselves all around the camp" (Num. 11:31-32). The phenomenon described here still occurs today, for a flock of migrating quails is no match for a strong contrary wind. They formed a layer three feet deep, and the smallest portion gathered by one man was, to translate "ten homers" conservatively, thirty-eight modern bushels.

MIXED BLESSING

But the Lord did not allow this feast to be held without an accompanying punishment: "While the meat was yet between their teeth, before it was consumed, the anger of the Lord was kindled against the people, and the Lord smote the people with a very great plague" (Num. 11:33). In this connection it should be mentioned that quails are known to carry a virus infection, and there are modern instances of people becoming quite ill from eating them.

These two events from the Exodus were remembered later by a psalmist, who wrote: "They asked, and he brought quails, and gave them bread from heaven in abundance" (Ps. 105:40). His poetic account interprets the quail feasts as examples of God's mercy in the wilderness—as a completely beneficial blessing rather than as the mixed blessing it seems to have been. In contrast, the psalmist in Psalm 78 says that during the feast "the anger of God rose against them and he slew the strongest of them, and laid low the picked men of Israel" (Ps. 78:31; cf. Ps. 106:13-15). Apparently the different ways of recollecting the quail feasts depend upon the purposes of the psalmists in reminding the people of their history.

The Raven

The word "raven" is used loosely to refer either to a particular genus (*Corvus*) or to any member of a large family called the Corvidae, a grouping that includes the largest perching birds—crows, rooks, jackdaws, magpies, jays, and choughs—representatives of which are found everywhere in the world except New Zealand. Thus the Bible speaks of "every raven according to its kind" in forbidding the Israelites to eat them (Lev. 11:15). In Palestine eight species are found—three ravens, two jackdaws, one crow, one rook, and one chough—but the two most frequently seen are the common raven, a completely black bird with a purplish cast, and the slightly grayish hooded crow. They are found everywhere, from the trackless rocky wastes south of the Dead Sea to Lebanon and Mount Hermon in the north.

At eventide ravens gather in large flocks in the rocky ravines that are so plentiful in Palestine; the Old Testament speaks of "ravens of the valley" (Prov. 30:17). Here they build their

CLASSIFICATION. *Corvus corax* (common raven), *Corvus cornix* (hooded crow), both members of Corvidae family of suborder Passeres (songbirds) of order Passeriformes (perching birds).
LEXICON. *Hebrew:* OREB. *Greek:* KORAX.

nests and raise their young without fear of being disturbed. The raven's fondness for dwelling in deserted regions was noted by Isaiah in his description of the Lord's judgment upon doomed Edom: "The owl and the raven shall dwell in it" (Isa. 34:11). Where once there was human activity, there would be only emptiness and ruins. Zephaniah speaks likewise of the raven that will "croak on the threshold" of the ruined city of Nineveh (Zeph. 2:14).

FIRST BIRD IN BIBLE

The raven is the first bird to be mentioned by name in the Bible, edging out the dove by a few verses in the story of the Flood. Here we read that "at the end of forty days Noah opened the window of the ark which he had made, and sent forth a raven; and it went to and fro until the waters were dried up from the earth" (Gen. 8:6-7). Noah may not have been an ornithologist, but he was certainly wise to choose this bird for the first reconnoitering mission. A robust bird with tremendous endurance, the raven is accustomed to roam far from its home base in search of food. That it did not return to the ark was a good sign, indicating that at least the raven could find food and also a place to rest on the dry mountain tops.

The Hebrew name for the raven, *oreb*, literally means "the black one." The author of the Song of Solomon, with his fine feeling for color, naturally saw a similarity between the glossy black feathers of the raven and the hair color of the beloved: "His locks are wavy, black as a raven" (Song of Sol. 5:11).

NASTY BIRDS

Several kinds of ravens, among them crows, are rather nasty predatory birds. Some are in the habit of attacking smaller and weaker creatures by pecking out their eyes, a practice noted in Proverbs: "The eye that mocks a father and scorns to obey a mother will be picked out by the ravens of the

This Byzantine mosaic at Ravenna gives us a vivid and comprehensive picture of the latter days of the Flood. As Noah reaches out to receive the dove with its olive branch, the raven has found a perch on a floating corpse. (Photograph courtesy of Alinari, Florence.)

valley" (Prov. 30:17). As in many other passages where unsavory creatures appear, the writers are often at pains to point out that even a bird of prey is a necessary part of God's kingdom, is under his care, and may be used to carry out his will. When the voice from the whirlwind speaks to Job, it inquires: "Who provides for the raven its prey, when its young ones cry to God, and wander about for lack of food?" (Job 38:41). This rhetorical question is answered in a psalm: "He [that is, the Lord] gives to the beasts their food, and to the young ravens which cry" (Ps. 147:9). And when Jesus wanted to impress upon his disciples that they should not spend their lives worrying about trivia, he chose the raven to illustrate his point: "Consider the ravens: they neither sow nor reap, they have neither storehouse nor barn, and yet God feeds them" (Luke 12:24).

The Sparrow

The word "sparrow" at one time meant any small bird, and it is probably in this sense that "birds" is most often to be understood when it appears in the Bible. The Hebrew word *tsippor* (literally, "the whistler" or "chirper") is usually translated simply as "bird," and only twice (in both the RSV and KJV) as "sparrow." Nevertheless, it is quite possible that a particular species of bird is referred to in these instances, probably that known as the house sparrow—the familiar small brown bird of the city.

A very common bird in Europe and adjacent areas, the house sparrow is now found throughout the world, frequently in former British colonies where it was introduced by early settlers. It did not reach the United States until the 1850's, but is known in this country as the English sparrow. The English or house sparrow is found in Palestine as well, especially around populated areas along the coast. It prefers to live near human beings and even to build its nest in their

CLASSIFICATION. *Passer domesticus* (house sparrow), *Passer salicarius* (Spanish sparrow), both members of subfamily Passerinae (sparrows and weavers) of Ploceidae family (Old World seed-eaters) of suborder Passeres (songbirds) of order Passeriformes (perching birds).
LEXICON. *Hebrew:* TSIPPOR. *Greek:* STROUTHION.

dwellings. In the interior of Palestine another kind of sparrow has been observed, the so-called "Spanish sparrow." These sparrows appear in such large numbers that the branches of trees are often bent by the weight of their nests, which are built close together.

LIVE BIRDS SOLD

In the market places of the Near East small boys offer live sparrows for sale. The birds are tied together in groups of from four to six by strings attached to one leg, and fly about over the boys' heads. Apparently much the same sight was

This highly realistic relief of the house sparrow is a plaster model made by a sculptor. It was found in Egypt and dates from the Ptolemaic period, a few centuries before the birth of Christ. (Photograph courtesy of the Metropolitan Museum of Art; Rogers Fund, 1907.)

common in New Testament times; when Jesus wanted to illustrate the fatherly care with which God looks after his creatures, he said: "Are not two sparrows sold for a penny? And not one of them will fall to the ground without your Father's will (Matt. 10:29). In Luke's account the details differ, but the message is the same: "Are not five sparrows sold for two pennies? And not one of them is forgotten before God" (Luke 12:6). Without much doubt, then, the Greek word *strouthion* refers here to the sparrow rather than just to any small bird in general.

CONTEXT DETERMINES

In the Old Testament one must let the context determine whether or not the sparrow is specifically meant. For instance, when the poet speaks about "a lonely bird on the housetop" (Ps. 102:7), he could hardly mean the gregarious sparrow. (There have been conjectures that the bird in this passage might be a thrush.) However, in the two instances that *tsippor* is mentioned with the swallow (q.v.), the RSV translators apparently feel that "sparrow" is the correct, or at least the preferred, rendering.

In both of these cases a trait of the sparrow is mentioned. "Like a sparrow in its flitting, like a swallow in its flying, a curse that is causeless does not alight," says a proverbist (Prov. 26:2), and "flitting" is an apt description of the sparrow's flight. One psalmist gives this poetic picture of a sparrow that has built its nest in the forecourt of the Temple: "Even the sparrow finds a home, and the swallow a nest for herself, where she may lay her young, at thy altars, O Lord of hosts" (Ps. 84:3). Not only does the sparrow show its "piety" here, but the Temple would be a natural place for a house sparrow to build its nest, just as natural as the sparrow's present-day choice of city hall.

The Stork

"Even the stork in the heavens knows her times . . . but my people know not the ordinance of the Lord" (Jer. 8:7). Thus the prophet complains of the obstinate blindness of his people, and in doing so employs the image of a migrating stork. And in fact, the white stork—the common stork which is still to be seen nesting on farmhouse roofs in the countryside of Europe —does pass through Palestine on its way to southern Africa in the fall, and on the way back in the spring. Some even make their nests and spend the summer in the Holy Land instead of crossing the Mediterranean.

There, instead of perching on rooftops, they prefer to nest in the tops of tall trees, a habit noted in one of the psalms: "The stork has her home in the fir trees" (Ps. 104:17). Every year the trekking stork searches out an old nest, preferably

---

CLASSIFICATION. *Ciconia ciconia* (white stork), member of Ciconiidae family of order Ciconiiformes (long-legged wading birds).
LEXICON. *Hebrew:* CHASIDAH.

its own, which it then repairs and makes additions to. Thus one may find storks' nests that are a hundred years old and have reached a height of more than three feet. The Hebrew name for stork means literally the "kindly one" or the "loyal one." Behind this nomenclature is an astute observaton on the way this bird cares for its young. As a rule, there are four young storks in a brood, and their need for food is so great that both parents are kept busy all summer simply flying back and forth to the nest to feed them. Later on, when the young storks are ready to fly, the parents conduct regular training sessions that continue until the young are ready to "solo" and the family's long flight to their winter home in southern Africa can begin.

NO DELICACY

Storks are characterized by their considerable height (about forty inches), their long, pointed beaks, and their long, thin legs. They feed on frogs, grass snakes, and small fish that they find in their favorite hunting grounds—brooks, ponds, and marshes. They will also eat insects. They do not themselves make good eating, so the Israelites were not being deprived of a delicacy when they were forbidden to eat storks' flesh (Lev. 11:19; Deut. 14:18). The white stork is named for its body color, but it actually cuts quite a flashy figure: the beak and legs are bright red, and the flight feathers of the wings are black.

MAJESTIC FLYERS

One biblical writer had an eye for the beauty and majestic calm of a stork in flight—an impressive sight indeed, for the bird has a wingspan of nearly six feet. When Zechariah attempted to describe one of his divine visions, he made it more vivid by calling up the image of a flying stork: "Behold, two women coming forward! The wind was in their wings; they had wings like the wings of a stork" (Zech. 5:9).

Called the "kindly one" or the "loyal one," the familiar white stork occasionally summers in the Holy Land. (Photograph courtesy of the Chicago Natural History Museum.)

183

The Swallow
The Swift

The swallow and the swift should not, from a zoological point of view, be treated under one heading, for they belong to entirely different orders. Although they are somewhat similar in appearance, the swallows (sometimes called "martins") are a family within the large order of perching birds, while the swift family belongs to a fairly small order that also includes the hummingbirds. From a language point of view, however, the two birds need to be discussed together.

In the RSV two Hebrew words, *deror* and *sus*, are translated as "swallow," and the swift is not mentioned at all; nevertheless, it is quite possible that the word *sus* means the swift. There is even some question as to whether *deror* means swallow, but the evidence seems sufficient to support this translation. The Hebrew word is derived from a root that means "to release," and it is true that the swallow, unlike

---

CLASSIFICATION. Hirundinidae family (swallows and martins) of suborder Passeres (songbirds) of order Passeriformes (perching birds). *Apus apus* (common Old World swift), member of Apodidae family of order Apodiformes.

LEXICON. *Hebrew:* DEROR (swallow); SUS (swallow or swift).

---

many other songbirds, does not thrive in captivity. The name also recognizes the fast, unrestrained, and graceful flight of this bird, a trait also hinted at in Proverbs, where the swallow's style of flying is compared with that of the sparrow (q.v.): "Like a sparrow in its flitting, like a swallow in its flying, a curse that is causeless does not alight" (Prov. 26:2).

SWALLOW

Elsewhere a Hebrew poet mentions the two birds together in his passionate longing for the Temple: "Even the sparrow finds a home, and the swallow a nest for herself, where she may lay her young, at thy altars, O Lord of hosts, my king and my God" (Ps. 84:3). Swallows are not the least hesitant about locating their nests next to or in barns, stables, and even houses. These nests are built of clay, sand, or manure mixed with the birds' saliva and pasted to a vertical surface. Seventy-nine species of the swallow are known, and it is impossible to determine which may have been familiar to biblical writers.

SWIFT

The common Old World swift is native to Palestine, and in the Jordan Valley one can encounter them in large flocks. The word *sus* is found in two places in the Old Testament, and one of these would lead us to prefer the rendering of "swift" rather than "swallow." Quoting the prayer of the ailing king of Judah, Hezekiah, Isaiah says: "Like a swallow [swift?] or a crane I clamor, I moan like a dove" (Isa. 38:14). The somewhat sharp chirp of the swallow is not a very striking simile for the plaint of the distraught king. In contrast, the swift has a soft, delicate voice, and its cry could easily be interpreted as a melodious wailing. The word *sus* also appears in Jeremiah's plaint: "Even . . . the turtledove, swallow [swift?], and crane keep the time of their coming; but my people know not the ordinance of the Lord" (Jer. 8:7). Here either bird suits the context, for both are migratory.

A swallow (right) and a swift are shown flying
together here for purposes of comparison, although
it is improbable that they would ever be seen thus.
(Drawing by Carol Wilde.)

The Vulture

Vultures have always had an unsavory reputation, and in the Bible there is nothing to elevate their status. Several kinds of vultures are prohibited as food in the Mosaic dietary laws (Lev. 11:13, 18; Deut. 14:12, 17), and in its other biblical appearances the vulture is seen in a sinister context or in connection with its habit of feeding primarily on carrion—including human corpses.

Three, possibly four, Hebrew words are used to denote different species of the Old World vultures, a subfamily of the same family that includes hawks, kites, and eagles. (Old World vultures are not to be confused with those found in the Western hemisphere, which are also carrion-eaters but belong to the Cathartidae family.) The word *racham* is translated "vulture" or "carrion vulture" in the RSV and as "gier

---

CLASSIFICATION. *Gyps fulvus fulvus* (Griffon vulture), *Neophron percnopterus* (Egyptian vulture or Pharaoh's hen), *Aegypius monachus* (black, or cinereous, vulture), all members of subfamily Aegypinae (Old World vultures); *Gypaetus barbatus aureus* (lammergeier, lamb-vulture, or ossifrage), member of subfamily Milvinae (or Gypaetinae); both subfamilies of Accipitridae family of order Falconiformes.

LEXICON. *Hebrew:* NESHER, RACHAM, PERES, OZNIYYAH.

eagle" in the KJV; *nesher,* usually meaning eagle (q.v.) and always translated thus in the KJV, is rendered "vulture" in the RSV to suit certain contexts; *peres* is "ossifrage" in the KJV and in one RSV reference, "vulture" in the other. In addition, *ozniyyah,* rendered "osprey" in both versions, may also mean a kind of vulture.

Only educated guesses are possible in trying to determine what species are meant in all these cases, for the Israelites

To the ancient Egyptians the vulture, along with other birds and mammals, represented a deity. This wall painting from a Theban temple of the Eighteenth Dynasty shows the vulture goddess Nekhbet of El Kab in a characteristically stylized pose. (Photograph courtesy of the Metropolitan Museum of Art.)

were undoubtedly familiar with many kinds of vultures that made their homes in Palestine, Egypt, and the nearby deserts. One that lives in Palestine today is the Griffon vulture, which is found especially in the region of the Sea of Galilee. It is a light brown bird with a pale yellow head and neck that are almost bare, being covered with only a very fine down. Enormously voracious, the Griffon vulture can be seen searching for dead animals from high in the air, then swooping down to rip open the belly of a corpse and consume the entrails.

OMINOUS SIGHT

It may be this bird that is meant by *nesher* wherever this word is not to be understood as referring to the eagle. In his denunciation of his fellow countrymen, Hosea speaks for the Lord saying: "Set the trumpet to your lips, for a vulture is over the house of the Lord, because they have broken my covenant, and transgressed my law" (Hos. 8:1). The ominous nature of a vulture's appearance in the sky is quite suitable here, for the prophet is emphasizing that disobedience of the Lord defiles any lip service that may be paid him in the Temple. Another passage where *nesher* is properly translated as "vulture" is Prov. 30:17, where reference is made to plucking out the eyes of a corpse (see p. 139). However, in the speech of God to Job, the RSV translators have chosen to use "eagle" where "vulture" might be a bit more apt: "Is it at your command that the eagle mounts up and makes his nest on high? On the rock he dwells and makes his home in the fastness of the rocky crag. Thence he spies out the prey; his eyes behold it afar off. His young ones suck up blood; and where the slain are, there is he" (Job 39:27-30). The first lines here might well refer to either the eagle or the vulture, but the final sentence suits the vulture better. On the battlefield, "where the slain are," it is the vulture who is active, whereas the eagle will touch carrion only in extreme circumstances. On the other hand, the RSV offers the following translation of Lam. 4:19:

"Our pursuers were swifter than the vultures in the heavens."
Here the eagle would seem more suitable, for it often serves
as a symbol of swiftness in the Old Testament.

PHARAOH'S HEN

The other Hebrew words for vultures are clustered in the
Mosaic dietary laws and appear nowhere else in the Bible, making positive identification even more difficult. Possibly *racham*
is the Egyptian vulture, also known as Pharaoh's hen, and
ozniyyah may refer not to the osprey (or fish hawk) but to
the black, or cinereous, vulture. The word *peres* may denote
the lammergeier, known also as the lamb-vulture or the ossifrage. This bird actually is not a vulture at all, even though
it will eat carrion, but is a very large kite (some authorities
classify it as a separate subfamily of the Accipitridae). It has
a unique way of killing its prey: since its beak is not particularly powerful, it carries its victim high in the air and then
drops it on the rocks. For this reason it is called the ossifrage,
which means literally "bone-breaker."

Insects

The Ant

The ant is mentioned only twice in the Bible, both times in the book of Proverbs, where we are given the advice: "Go to the ant, O sluggard; consider her ways, and be wise. Without having any chief, officer or ruler, she prepares her food in summer, and gathers her sustenance in harvest" (Prov. 6:6-8; cf. Prov. 30:24-25). This advice is still sound today, for the ant is one of the most fascinating of all living creatures. It is what is known as a "social" insect, one which lives in well-ordered colonies, and its instincts provide it with a harmonious society that in many respects puts man, the "social animal," to shame.

CASTE SOCIETY

Ants are born into one of three distinct castes: the female, or queen; the sterile female, or worker; and the male. The proverbist is not quite accurate when he declares that ants have no "chief, officer or ruler," for the winged female ant, the queen, whose chief function is to lay eggs and replenish and increase the population of the colony, is the key member

---

CLASSIFICATION. *Messor semirufus* (harvester ant), member of Formicidae family (ants) of order Hymenoptera (bees, wasps, ants).
LEXICON. *Hebrew:* NEMALAH.

of ant society. She does not actually "rule" as a queen in the human sense of the word, since the other members of the colony go about their tasks without any urging, but she is rewarded for her procreative efforts with "the life of a queen," as specialized worker ants feed her and attend to her every need.

WORKERS

Of necessity, the worker caste far outnumbers the queen caste, and it is the worker that, as the name implies, carries out all the menial duties connected with the construction and maintenance of the colony and the obtaining of food. Within the caste are subdivisions: some workers, with especially well-developed jaws that serve as weapons, are the soldiers who defend the colony; others are merely food-gatherers, who are capable of carrying food in their stomachs for other members of the colony. The third caste, the male, performs only one task—that of mating with the queen. It is not equipped to be a worker, but like the queen it has wings, for the mating takes place in flight.

INTELLIGENT?

It is difficult to reject the idea that ants possess a certain amount of intelligence. Their building activities seem to indicate this, for the dwellings that ant colonies construct are highly sophisticated. It is just as inconceivable that man by instinct alone could build and furnish a large city as it is to presume that ants, without understanding and judgment, could build an anthill with its various chambers, halls, pillars, galleries, corridors, and so forth. Ant workers may live to be as much as fourteen years old, and older workers have been observed rejecting, tearing down, and rebuilding walls constructed by younger workers. Evidently they can "teach" their skills by example.

The proverbist notes that the ant "prepares her food in

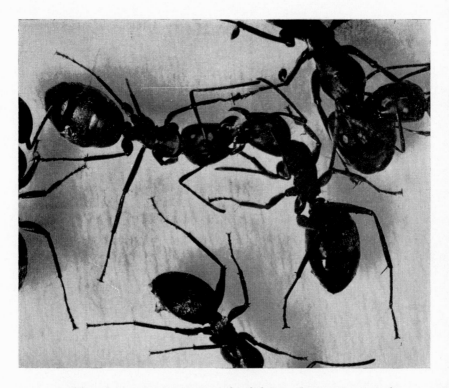

Although they may appear to be fighting, the two ants in the center of this picture are actually collaborating. The one on the right is transmitting food from its "social stomach" to another member of the colony. (Wide World Photos.)

summer, and gathers her sustenance in harvest," which would seem to indicate that he had in mind a special kind of ant. Although some species raise "livestock," that is, plant lice or aphids, to provide food for the colony, other more primitive varieties are collectors, who feed on any edible morsel they find. Those "collector ants" that do not hibernate during the winter are obliged to "harvest" food in the fall and lay up a large enough supply to sustain the colony until spring. One of these, known appropriately enough as the harvester ant, is native to Palestine.

HARVESTER ANTS

As the time for farmers to gather in their crops approaches, harvester ants may be seen traveling in large detachments to the fields. Here they bite off seed pods and drag them home to the anthill, where another gang of workers receives them, removes the seeds from the pods, and discards the chaff in a heap next to the anthill. Then the cleaned seeds are taken below to special chambers that are kept aired and dry throughout the winter so that the seeds—the winter food supply—will not begin to sprout.

SLAVE-KEEPING ANTS

Certain species of ants are so "human" that they have developed a society as degenerate as some in our own history. These are the slave-keeping ants, who carry out raids on neighboring colonies and bring back the larvae and pupae of worker ants to be raised in servitude. In some instances the ruling classes of such societies have become so degenerate that they are unable even to feed themselves without the assistance of the slaves. On the whole, however, the hallmark of the ant is its industriousness and skill, and the words of the Hebrew proverbist may be particularly relevant to us, for we live in a time of history when such traits are not, perhaps, so highly regarded.

The Bee

The smallest "domestic animal" in the world is the honeybee, and it has perhaps been domesticated the longest, for forms of beekeeping can be traced back into the early history of man's culture. About 4000 B.C., during the First Dynasty in Egypt, the bee appears as a symbol in art, and an Egyptian relief sculpture from about 3000 B.C. shows a scene involving a process in beekeeping, the pressing of honey from honeycombs. In ancient Greece candles were made from beeswax, and in the old Nordic countries, as early as 800-500 B.C., mead, a drink concocted from fermented honey, was a common and highly favored beverage.

The bee is mentioned several times in the Bible, and its produce, honey and wax, much more frequently. It is not clear whether beekeeping was practiced in Israel, although some passages would seem to indicate that it was. Ezekiel mentions honey as a chief export of Palestine (Ezek. 27:17), and there are references to the fact that in the Near East the beekeeper attracts swarming bees by whistling or ringing bells:

CLASSIFICATION. *Apis mellifica syriaca* (honeybee native to Palestine), *Apis unicolor* (Egyptian bee), both members of Apoidea superfamily of order Hymenoptera (bees, wasps, ants).

LEXICON. *Hebrew:* DEBORAH.

197

"In that day the Lord will whistle . . . for the bee which is in the land of Assyria" (Isa. 7:18). Many authorities, however, believe that beekeeping was not known in Palestine until the Hellenistic period, about 300 B.C.

"SOCIAL" INSECTS

Belonging to the same zoological order as the ant and the hornet (q.q.v.), that of veined-wing insects, honeybees are, like many varieties of hornets and ants, social insects. Their caste system is similar to that of the ants, and a typical hive, or society, consists of from sixty to seventy thousand individuals: one queen; five to six hundred males, or drones; the rest workers. In human terms, the workers constitute the proletariat and the drones the wealthy and highborn leisure class. The queen has no human counterpart, for she is the mother of all, the source of life and actual creator of the colony.

The life cycle of the bee begins with the queen, who during the warmer months of the year produces up to two hundred thousand eggs, laying the largest number in midsummer, when a single day's production can be more than seventeen thousand. Naturally, when the eggs are hatched and the bees begin to reach maturity, a "population explosion" occurs in the hive, but bees are endowed with instincts that prevent utter confusion from reigning. A new queen is among the eggs that are hatched, and when she is about to emerge, the old queen, along with a large contingent of the old workers, leaves the hive to search for a new home to begin a new hive. Where beekeepers have not constructed hives to accommodate these swarms, the bees find a place in a hollow tree, a cleft of rock, a hole in the ground, or even, as is suggested by the story of Samson (Judg. 14:8), inside a carcass. But a wise beekeeper knows when the swarming time will occur, and prepares his hives so that he may capitalize on the wax and honey that bees produce.

Beeswax is a kind of "sweat" secreted by glands in the rear

Not only was the bee well known in ancient Egypt, it also formed a part of their hieroglyphic alphabet, as shown here in an enlarged section of a wall relief. It should be pointed out that even though this hieroglyph has a certain amount of detail, the bee, like other insects, actually has six legs. (Photograph courtesy of the Oriental Institute of the University of Chicago.)

199

part of the bee's body; it is the material used in the building of the honeycomb, a network of cells in which eggs develop into the larvae and where honey, the staple food of the bee, is stored. In turn, the wax is produced in the bee's body from the honey it eats; it has been estimated that a bee colony eats twenty pounds of honey for each pound of wax produced. Honey itself is made from the nectar of flowers, and if one bee were to produce a single pound of honey, it would have to make about eighty thousand trips back and forth from the hive, in the process drawing nectar from three million flowers.

"FLOWING WITH . . . HONEY"

We may be sure that the ancient Israelites knew and appreciated the food value of honey. Although the Mosaic laws forbade the eating of the bees themselves, as well as most other insects, honey was not forbidden, apparently because it was considered to be essentially a product of plants and flowers rather than a bodily secretion. Thus there are many favorable references to honey, beginning with the famous description of the Promised Land as a "land flowing with milk and honey" (Exod. 3:8). Later a poet sang of the fear of the Lord and the commandments of the Lord as being "sweeter also than honey and drippings of the honeycomb" (Ps. 19:10). And a Hebrew proverbist said: "My son, eat honey, for it is good, and the drippings of the honeycomb are sweet to your taste" (Prov. 24:13). When Jacob advised his sons on what gifts they should take to the ruler of Egypt, actually his son Joseph, he told them: "Take some of the choice fruits of the land in your bags, and carry down to the man a present, a little balm and a little honey . . ." (Gen. 43:11).

This honeybee, a member of the worker class, is shown making a "collection" from a flower. Besides collecting food for its colony, the bee is unwittingly picking up pollen from the flower. (Photograph courtesy of Ewing Galloway.)

Therefore, whether or not domestic honey was available to biblical peoples, wild honey certainly was, and a traveler in a Near Eastern wilderness would be on the lookout for caches of honey in rocky clefts and similar likely spots. In the song of Moses about the Lord's benevolences toward Israel, there is the declaration: "He made him suck honey out of the rock" (Deut. 32:13). A Hebrew poet sings: "O that my people would listen to me. . . . With honey from the rock I would satisfy you" (Ps. 81:13, 16). John the Baptist found such sustenance when he was in the rocky wilderness, for "his food was locusts and wild honey" (Matt. 3:4).

Honey had uses other than as a food; it was also an important material for embalming. Embalming was chiefly a practice of the ancient Egyptians, of course, but apparently was also employed by the Hebrews during their stay in Egypt, for Joseph had the body of his father Jacob embalmed, and later his own body was similarly preserved, to be carried out of Egypt many years later during the Exodus. In Egypt embalming was practiced as early as 3000 B.C. and was especially popular around 1300-1000 B.C., about the time of the Exodus. For rich people and pharaohs there was a very elaborate (and expensive) process, but for those of lesser means there were shorter methods, and it was here that honey was used.

ATTACKING BEES

Biblical writers were not unaware of one other facet of bees —their propensity for attacking in large swarms any person or animal who disturbs the hive. "The Amorites who lived in that hill country came out against you and chased you as bees do," says the author of the book of Deuteronomy (1:44), calling up a clear picture of an outnumbered army being put to flight. A Hebrew poet declares: "All the nations surrounded me . . . they surrounded me like bees" (Ps. 118:10-12). His words call up a vivid picture of a swarm of attacking bees, which seem to be everywhere.

The Flea

Wherever in the world human beings live, there also lives the flea. Especially where hygienic conditions are poor, this tiny bloodsucking parasite, which forms an order of insects of itself, thrives. Not surprisingly, the different species of flea are identified, at least in everyday language, according to the animal each species chooses as its host. Thus, although a dog or cat flea will attack man in the absence of its preferred host, there is a species known as the human flea, which singles out man for its attentions. One of the more devastating instances of a flea changing hosts occurred in the pestilence that ravaged Europe in the fourteenth century known as the Black Death. This disease actually attacks rats initially, but when infected rats entered human dwellings their fleas switched to human beings and thus transferred the virulent bacteria from blood stream to blood stream.

HUMAN HOST

The female of the human flea, which is somewhat larger than the male, lays about a dozen eggs twice a year in cracks between floor boards and in dirty corners of rooms. While mature fleas feed exclusively on the blood of host animals, the larvae may eat anything putrefactive, especially animal

---

CLASSIFICATION. *Pulex irritans* (human flea), member of Pulicidae family of order Siphonaptera.

LEXICON. *Hebrew:* PAROSH.

Here greatly magnified, the flea still appears less harmful than it actually is. Though none of its legs are highly developed like those of the grasshopper, this insect has extraordinary leaping powers. (Drawing by Carol Wilde.)

excrement. For an insect its size, the flea has a relatively long life span, and some have been known to live for as long as five hundred days.

"AFTER A FLEA!"

Apparently people of biblical times took little note of the flea, since it is of such an insignificant size. Where it is mentioned, this "insignificance" is stressed. During David's flight from the enraged King Saul he approached the sleeping king and cut off a piece of his robe. The next day, in order to illustrate that he was not seeking Saul's life, David held up the fragment of cloth and shouted from a distance: "After whom has the king of Israel come out? After whom do you pursue? . . . After a flea!" (I Sam. 24:14). By comparing himself to the lowest form of life known at the time, David was trying to convince Saul that he had no pretensions to power, and that the king was wasting his strength chasing after someone so unworthy of his attention.

The Fly

Flies are mentioned frequently in the Bible, and since several Hebrew words are used to denote them, there seems to be little doubt that the biblical authors discerned among several species of the many that thrive in the Near East. Probably the chief of these, and the most widely distributed kind of fly today, is the common housefly, which also happens to be one of man's most dangerous enemies.

The fly is the bearer of harmful bacteria and therefore a spreader of disease, for it goes about depositing its eggs—and collecting germs—in unsanitary places, such as garbage heaps, sewers, and carcasses. Compounding this danger is its enormous power of reproduction, an ability shared by all flies. It has been estimated that if all the offspring of a single summer were to live (which, fortunately, does not happen), one fly would have five billion descendants to its name. The fly is not only highly fertile, but it also takes only a very short time for the fly to reach maturity. Given favorable circum-

---

CLASSIFICATION. *Musca domestica* (housefly), *Calliphora erythrocephala* (bluebottle), both members of Muscidae family; *Stomoxys calcitrans* (tabanid or stable fly), and *Tabanus arenivagus* (horsefly), both members of Tabanidae family; *Hypoderma bovis* (cattlebot), *Gastrophilus equi* (horsebot), *Oestrus ovis* (sheepbot), all members of Oestridae family; all three families of order Diptera (two-winged insects).

LEXICON. *Hebrew:* ZEBUB (housefly?); QERETS (botfly?); AROB (swarms of flies); RIMMAH (maggot, larva).

205

The common housefly, *Musca domestica,* is a familiar sight, but is not often seen so close up. Because of its habits it is more than just an annoying pest, for it spreads a variety of diseases. (Photograph courtesy of Ewing Galloway.)

stances of warmth and moisture, eggs hatch a few hours after being laid; the larvae, or maggots, become pupae in four days, and the pupae become adults in about a week. From egg to mature fly, the whole process takes only ten or eleven days.

Another type of fly represented in the Near East is the botfly, a two-winged insect that causes much grief to livestock by irritating them and also by spreading disease. Thus they are classified according to the livestock they prefer to pester: there are cattlebots, horsebots, and sheepbots. The cattlebot deposits its eggs—about six hundred of them—deep in the fur of a cow, usually on one of its legs. When after a few days they have hatched, they are either licked off by the cow or succeed in boring through the animal's hide to begin their peregrinations through the body. After a few months the larvae settle down under the skin of the animal's back. Here the larvae, which have now attained a length of three-eights of an inch, burrow part of the way back through the skin and form a capsule—the so-called "spring boil." From May to July the larvae attain their full growth and at length bore completely through the skin to fall to the ground, where they pupate. The pupal stage lasts one month; then, on a warm summer's day a new botfly breaks its casing, ready to start another life cycle.

The Old Testament mentions both of these common insects, the housefly and the botfly. For instance, the Preacher says: "Dead flies make the perfumer's ointment give off an evil odor; so a little folly outweighs wisdom and honor" (Eccles. 10:1). Jeremiah is one of several biblical authors familiar with the cattlebot. In his prophecy concerning Nebuchadnezzar's attack on Egypt he says: "A beautiful heifer is Egypt, but a gadfly [botfly] from the north has come upon her" (Jer. 46:20).

FOURTH PLAGUE

It is difficult to determine what kind of fly ravaged Egypt during the fourth plague, when Moses was struggling to obtain the freedom of his people. Suggested possibilities, chosen from types that presently exist in the area, include the housefly, the bluebottle, and the tabanid fly, a classification which includes the horsefly and the dreaded tsetse fly of the tropics, carrier of sleeping sickness. In any case, "there came great swarms of flies into the house of Pharaoh and into his servants' houses, and in all the land of Egypt the land was ruined by reason of the flies" (Exod. 8:24). There is a certain logic in the way that this plague followed the plague of the frogs (q.v.) and the plague of gnats (q.v.). The second plague had seen dead frogs collected in large rotting heaps, the foul smell of which pervaded the land. Such heaps of decaying animal matter would provide ideal breeding places for flies. Equally logical is that the plague following that of the flies involved disease, for flies are notorious carriers of harmful bacteria. "The hand of the Lord will fall with a very severe plague upon your cattle which are in the field, the horses, the asses, the camels, the herds, and the flocks" (Exod. 9:3). Thus the livestock of the Egyptians was afflicted, and soon afterward the Egyptians themselves were prey to "boils breaking out in sores on man and beast throughout all the land of Egypt" (Exod. 9:9).

WORMS AND MAGGOTS

In addition to these biblical references to adult flies, there are numerous mentions of worms. Almost without exception, it would seem, biblical writers meant by "worm" that stage of the fly's life cycle which we call the "maggot," that is, the larval stage, and not the common earthworm, which is not even distantly related to the insects. Such is the case when "worms" are mentioned in connection with corpses, for earthworms have no interest in decaying flesh and obtain sustenance from vegetable matter in the earth. For example, the KJV and RSV use the translation "worms" when Job says: "They lie down alike in the dust, and the worms cover them" (Job 21:26). There seems little doubt here that a better rendering of the Hebrew word would be "maggot," a usage employed in the RSV in Isaiah's taunting song upon the death of the cruel king of Babylon: "Your pomp is brought down to Sheol, the sound of your harps; maggots are the bed beneath you, and worms are your covering" (Isa. 14:11).

During the Exodus an incident occurred in which food was

spoiled by worms, again undoubtedly fly larvae: "But they did not listen to Moses; some left part of it [the manna] till the morning, and it bred worms and became foul" (Exod. 16:20). This food spoilage did not affect the portion that upon the command of Moses had been set aside for the Sabbath (Exod. 16:24). The explanation of this odd favoritism may be that, fearing the anger of Moses, the Israelites hid the forbidden manna in the darkest corners of their tents, exactly where flies would be able to get at it and deposit their eggs; in contrast, manna stored legally for the Sabbath would be kept in the open where it could be protected.

Other insect larvae besides those of the fly apparently go under the name "worm" in the Bible, but it is impossible, except in the most general way, to identify them. The Mosaic law mentions one such creature in connection with the curses that will afflict those who do not keep the law: "You shall plant vineyards and dress them, but you shall neither drink of the wine nor gather the grapes; for the worm shall eat them" (Deut. 28:39). This may be a butterfly larva of the leaf-roller family, which we know as the "worm" in apples.

THE APPOINTED WORM

A celebrated story involving an insect larva is told in the book of Jonah. After the city of Nineveh repented as a result of the judgment preached by Jonah, the formerly reluctant prophet was piqued by God's mercy. He could not really believe, however, that God would spare the city, and so he sat on a height overlooking the city to have a grandstand seat for the spectacle of its destruction. One night the Lord let a castor oil plant grow up to provide shade for Jonah's head. "But when dawn came up the next day, God appointed a worm which attacked the plant, so that it withered" and the prophet had no more shade for his bald pate (Jonah 4:7-11). There is a possibility that Jonah received his lesson on mercy through the instrument of an insect larva called *Rhyncetus betuleti.*

The Gnat

The very large order of two-winged insects (Diptera) includes many varieties that are harmful to man, both as pests and as disease carriers. Not only are the larger representatives of the order, the flies (q.v.), harmful, but so are several families of small slender insects with large antennae—principally the gnats, mosquitoes, and sand flies. Gnats are not often mentioned in the Bible, making it impossible to form a definite identification of species, but it is not surprising to find them involved in the plagues that beset Egypt while the Pharaoh stubbornly refused to release the people of Israel.

The King James Version calls the third plague a plague of lice, but the RSV's "gnats" would seem to be a better rendering. "Mosquitoes" is another possibility: the family that includes the familiar anopheles mosquito is known for depositing its eggs in water. It will be recalled that the first plague had caused the water in the land of Egypt to turn to blood, killing the fish. Since Pharaoh's magicians were able to dupli-

---

CLASSIFICATION. Some species of genus *Anopheles* (anopheles mosquitoes), members of Culicidae family; *Trichotanypus tiberiae* (harvester gnat), member of Chironomidae family (midges); some species of genus *Phlebotomus* (sand flies), members of Psychodidae family (moth flies); all three families of suborder Nematocera of order Diptera (two-winged insects).

LEXICON. *Hebrew:* KEN, KINNAM. *Greek:* KONOPS.

---

cate this event, it is not impious to suggest that Moses and Aaron had placed some poisonous chemical in the water, causing it to turn red. Thereafter, the frogs, no longer able to stay in their natural habitat near the water, came up on dry land—the second plague, and one that the magicians could also duplicate.

GNAT, MOSQUITO, OR SAND FLY?

But then came the third plague, one which was beyond the magicians: "Aaron stretched out his hand with his rod, and struck the dust of the earth, and there came gnats on man and beast; all the dust of the earth became gnats throughout all the land of Egypt" (Exod. 8:17). This plague can be considered a logical consequence of the earlier plagues. With the fish dead and the frogs gone to dry land, the natural enemies of the mosquito had disappeared: the mosquito larvae on which they would have fed developed unimpeded into adults. This plague is perhaps the first recorded example of the balance of nature being upset. In any case, the insects seemed as numerous as the particles of dust in the land. In present-day Egypt swarms of mosquitoes and gnats still appear regularly—swarms so huge and dense that they darken the sun.

The anopheles mosquito, carrier of malaria and yellow fever, may not have been the "gnat" of the third plague. A strong possibility is that it was a species of the sand fly. If so, then the plague was a fearful one indeed, for this tiny member of the moth-fly family has a far more painful bite than the mosquito. Furthermore, it does not betray itself by a buzzing noise in flight, and is so small that it penetrates most mosquito nettings. Mosquito nettings were not, incidentally, unknown in biblical times: the apocryphal book of Judith mentions one that was woven "with purple and gold and emeralds and precious stones" (Jth. 10:21). One other possibility is that the insect in question was the harvester gnat, in which case the plague would have been considerably more bearable. This tiny member of the midge family makes a nuisance of itself by flying into the nose and mouth of an animal or human being, but does not bite.

STRAINING GNATS

The New Testament refers to the gnat only once, when Jesus says scornfully to the scribes and Pharisees: "You blind guides, straining out a gnat and swallowing a camel!" (Matt. 23:24). It was common practice among the Jews to filter

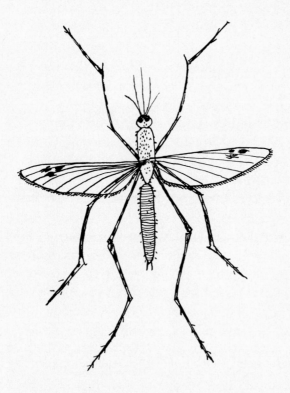

This drawing of a typical mosquito gives one a good idea of the characteristics of the general grouping that includes gnats, mosquitoes, and sand flies; note the long, slender body and pronounced antennae. (Drawing by Carol Wilde.)

wine before it was served by pouring it through a piece of cloth to remove any insects or other impurities. Jesus is telling the Pharisees that their fastidious attention to such tiny impurities prevents them from recognizing an absurdly large impurity, symbolized here by the camel (q.v.).

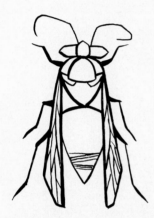

The Hornet

Hornets and wasps comprise another major family in the order of insects that also includes bees and ants. They are larger than their relatives, and in many ways more impressive, especially in regard to physical appearance. The most common hornet found in biblical lands today is the *Vespa orientalis,* a large, yellow and reddish-brown insect that preys upon honeybees, frequently ambushing workers as they make their rounds from flower to flower. The *orientalis,* like many species in its family, is a social insect in the manner of bees and ants (q.q.v.). A queen provides the beginning of a colony when she begins constructing, cell by cell, a "paper" nest

---

CLASSIFICATION. *Vespa orientalis,* member of Vespidae family (hornets and wasps) of order Hymenoptera (bees, wasps, ants).
LEXICON. *Hebrew:* TSIRAH.

(actually masticated wood pulp). As soon as a few cells are ready, she lays eggs in them; then she goes on to build more cells, lay more eggs, and so on. After the larvae are hatched, she feeds them until they reach adulthood and can aid in the building of the nest.

When the nest has reached maximum development it may contain about sixteen thousand cells. Since each cell can be used three times for hatching eggs, a single colony can produce fifty thousand hornets. For most of the spring and summer only sterile female workers are hatched; then, in late fall, males and fertile females appear. The males die immediately after mating, while the future queens hibernate under moss or beneath the bark of a tree. Meanwhile, the old colony perishes as cold weather approaches. In spring the cycle begins over again.

HORNET INVADERS

During the Israelites' sojourn in the wilderness after leaving Egypt, the Lord promised a striking form of aid in the forthcoming battles against the tribes inhabiting the Promised Land: "And I will send hornets before you, which shall drive out the Hivite, Canaanite, and Hittite from before you" (Exod. 23:28; cf. Deut. 7:20). Later, in his farewell address at Shechem, Joshua, the leader of the Israelites, speaks of the same promise as having been fulfilled: "Thus says the Lord, the God of Israel, '. . . I sent the hornet before you, which drove them out before you, the two kings of the Amorites; it was not by your sword or by your bow'" (Josh. 24:2, 12). Some interpreters believe that these passages must be understood metaphorically, with the hornet symbolizing a sudden

This rather unusual view of a hornets' nest, from the inside, was obtainable because it had been built against a window pane. The "paper-like" material from which it is constructed was manufactured by the queen of the colony. (Wide World Photos.)

fear that gripped the enemies of Israel. Others insist that the words ought to be taken literally, and with our knowledge of the hornet this latter interpretation is not impossible.

FEARLESS PREDATORS

Hornets are fearless and justly dreaded predatory insects. They are equipped with a poisonous sting with which they paralyze their victims; and, in contrast to the bee, whose stinger is barbed and thus breaks off the first time it is used, it has a smooth stinger that can be used again and again. Furthermore, to be stung by a hornet is much more painful than to be stung by a bee. Hornets are usually peaceable enough toward human beings and animals, but when they believe their nest is in danger, they swarm out in large numbers and recklessly attack the intruder. Both humans and animals have been stung to death during such encounters.

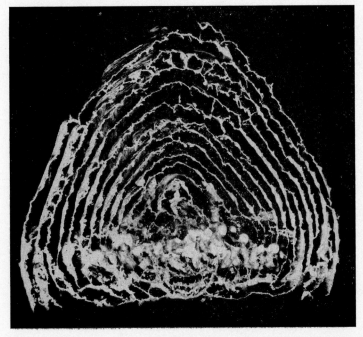

The Kermes

There is no specific mention in either the Old or New Testaments of the strange insect called the kermes, but there are a number of references to scarlet cloth. The dye that was used in the Near East to obtain this color was, and still is, manufactured by treating the dried bodies of the female kermes with vinegar. The end product is called either "crimson" or "scarlet" in the Bible. A primitive insect that appears to be more vegetable than animal, the kermes (sometimes called the "lac" or the "cochineal") is a nodelike creature, about the size of a pea, that attaches itself to the branches of the kermes oak. It is harvested for processing into dye during the month of May.

WEALTHY WORE SCARLET . . .

Like purple coloring (see "The Snail"), scarlet was a costly and fashionable dyestuff in biblical times, much used by the wealthy and thus associated with good living and well-being. It was a fortunate housewife who could be complimented for clothing "all her household . . . in scarlet" (Prov. 31:21). Scarlet cloth made with kermes dye does not become faded from exposure to sunlight or from washing. It is as impossible

---

CLASSIFICATION. *Kermes biblicus*, member of Kermesidae family of suborder Hermoptera of order Rhynchota.

LEXICON. *Hebrew:* SHANI, TOLAATH. *Greek:* KOKKINOS.

to bleach a scarlet cloth as it is to remove an indelible stain, and yet, in Isaiah's picture language, the Lord makes this impossible thing happen: "Come now, let us reason together, says the Lord: though your sins are like scarlet, they shall be as white as snow; though they are red like crimson, they shall become like wool" (Isa. 1:18)—man's sinfulness can be washed away by the mercy of the Lord.

ALSO SOLDIERS AND HARLOTS

While purple was the color of royal garments, soldiers were usually attired in scarlet. The prophet Nahum makes note of this in the case of the troops of the Assyrian king: "His soldiers are clothed in scarlet" (Nah. 2:3). Centuries later the soldiers who tortured Jesus apparently wore robes of the same color. Matthew relates that the soldiers "stripped him and put a scarlet robe upon him, and plaiting a crown of thorns they put it on his head, and put a reed in his right hand" (Matt. 27:28).

Like other fashionable garments, clothing of scarlet was worn not only by the rich and powerful, but also by the harlots. Jeremiah makes this plain in a picturesque description of such a woman: "And you, O desolate one, what do you mean that you dress in scarlet, that you deck yourself with ornaments of gold, that you enlarge your eyes with paint? In vain you beautify yourself. Your lovers despise you; they seek your life" (Jer. 4:30). And in Revelation there is the remarkable portrait of the harlot of Babylon, seated upon a scarlet beast and arrayed in purple and scarlet (Rev. 17:1-6). But when her city meets its doom, then the source of all the evil splendor of the world will be cut off: "And the merchants of the earth weep and mourn for her, since no one buys their cargo any more, cargo of gold, silver, jewels and pearls, fine linen, purple, silk and scarlet . . ." (Rev. 18:11-12). "Alas, alas, for the great city that was clothed in fine linen, in purple and scarlet" (Rev. 18:16).

The Locust

The straight-winged insects known either as locusts or grass-hoppers form another large grouping of which many varieties abound in the Holy Land. As a result there are numerous Hebrew words in the Bible for locusts and their relatives, and we can only make educated guesses as to what specific species each of these words meant. We can be fairly sure that reference is made to members of three related families: the locusts and grasshoppers, the crickets, and the katydids; among these, at least four different species are probably mentioned in the Old Testament, as well as names for the stages of development in the life cycle of these insects in general. Whatever the species, however, locusts are rarely mentioned with favor by biblical writers, for many of them destroy vegetation, including, of course, crops.

In spite of its destructiveness, several biblical references to

---

CLASSIFICATION. *Acridium peregrinum* (desert locust), *Anacridium aegyptium* (short-horned locust), *Tryxalis nasuta* (slant-faced locust), all members of Acrididae family; Tettigoniidae family (long-horned grasshoppers and katydids); some species of genus *Gryllotalpa* (mole crickets), members of Gryllidae family; all three families of order Orthoptera (straight-winged insects).

LEXICON. *Hebrew:* ARBEH, GOB, GEB (desert locust); CHAGAB (short-horned locust?); SOLAM (slant-faced locust?); CHARGOL (katydids?); TSELATSAL (mole cricket?); GAZAM, YELEQ, CHASIL (instars). *Greek:* AKRIS.

this insect portray it as being relatively harmless: these include many of the passages where the Hebrew word is translated "grasshopper," "bald locust," or "cricket" in English versions. It is suggested that the biblical writers meant specific species in these instances, including the short-horned locust ("grasshopper"), the katydids ("cricket" in RSV, "beetle" in KJV), and the mole cricket.

LOCUST PLAGUES

It is quite a different story with the desert locust, which is most likely the variety responsible for the various plagues of locusts mentioned in the Bible. In other instances the Bible uses the locust figuratively as a symbol of destruction and havoc. For example, Nahum forecasts the doom of Nineveh in such a manner: "There will the fire devour you, the sword will cut you off. It will devour you like the locust" (Nah. 3:15). This insect still appears in Mediterranean countries as a veritable scourge, and the ancient Israelites had ample opportunity to observe its appearance and habits, many of which are pointed out in the Bible. This species is a little over two inches long and has a wingspread of some five inches (it does not fly, however, using its wings only as a parachute when jumping). The back pair of legs are as long as the rest of its body and are equipped with powerful muscles, enabling the desert locust to leap enormously long distances. At rest, its hind legs protrude high above the rest of the body in an inverted V, but in "flight" they are on a plane with the body.

FORM MASSIVE HORDES

When desert locusts reach the stage when the urge to wander comes over them, usually in June or July, they form massive hordes and begin to move across the countryside, eating all the vegetation in their path. A classic description of such an invasion is given us in the story of the eighth plague against Egypt, just before the Exodus: "And when it was morning the east wind had brought the locusts. And the locusts came up over all the land of Egypt, and settled on the whole country of Egypt, such a dense swarm of locusts as had never been before, nor ever shall be again. For they covered the face of the whole land, so that the land was darkened, and they ate all the plants in the land and all the fruit of the trees which the hail had left; not a green thing remained, neither tree nor plant of the field, through all the land of Egypt" (Exod. 10:13-15; cf. Ps. 78:46; Rev. 9:3). This description of an invasion of locusts may seem exaggerated to someone who has never witnessed one, but it is quite accurate. Scientists have observed hordes of desert locusts crossing the Suez Canal simply by plunging into the water until a bridge of bodies is formed for the rest to cross.

COVER THE SUN

Fortunately, invasions of locusts do not occur often, but when they do, the effect is devastating. Huge swarms of locusts, looking from a distance like clouds that cover the sun, usually follow the prevailing wind. What remains after they pass is vividly described by Joel, who uses the scourge of the locust as a figure of the coming Day of the Lord, comparing the locusts to an army: "For a nation has come up against my land, powerful and without number; its teeth are lions' teeth, and it has the fangs of a lioness. It has laid waste my vines, and splintered my fig trees; it has stripped off their bark and thrown it down; their branches are made white" (Joel 1:6-7). It is an illustration very much to the point when, at other places in the Bible, enemy armies are compared to hordes of locusts (Judg. 6:5; 7:12; Jer. 46:23). No wonder Joel exclaims: "Hear this, you aged men, give ear, all inhabitants of the land! Has such a thing happened in your days, or in the days of your fathers?" (Joel 1:2).

Joel reveals a knowledge of the developmental stages of the locust when he says: "What the cutting locust left, the

The locusts, or grasshoppers, depicted in this Egyptian wall painting of the late Eighteenth Dynasty (fourteenth century B.C.) seem rather benign, but the artist had not, perhaps, witnessed an invasion of locusts. He has also shortened the hind legs so that his locusts might fit comfortably into the design. (Photograph courtesy of the Oriental Institute of the University of Chicago.)

swarming locust has eaten. What the swarming locust left, the hopping locust has eaten, and what the hopping locust left, the destroying locust has eaten" (Joel 1:4). Undoubtedly he is referring to the three stages of the locust's life during which it is particularly destructive. Just before the rainy season the female deposits, by means of an ovipositor, up to one hundred eggs in soft soil. The larvae appear in April or May, and pass through a series of stages, known as instars, until they are fully mature. Joel's "cutting locusts" are probably first instars, the "swarming locusts" middle instars, and the "destroying locusts" later but not yet fully mature instars. In its adult instars, the color of the locust is a reddish brown, which turns to yellow with a brownish network on the wings.

Amos was another prophet who observed that the locust is harmful even before it reaches the migratory stage, and that in its early and middle instars is capable of spoiling the spring harvest: "Thus the Lord God showed me: behold, he was forming locusts in the beginning of the shooting up of the latter growth; and lo, it was the latter growth after the king's mowings. When they had finished eating the grass of the land, I said, 'O Lord God, forgive, I beseech thee! How can Jacob stand? He is so small!' " (Amos 7:1-2).

ROASTED, BOILED, GROUND

People who live in the Near East are able to obtain some measure of good from the generally undesirable locust, for there it is used for food, especially by the Arabs. Locusts are readily available in Arabian markets; they are roasted, boiled, or dried and ground into a flour from which cakes are made. That the same use prevailed in biblical times, at least to some extent, is revealed by the Israelite dietary laws, which permitted the eating of certain kinds of locusts (Lev. 11:22). In New Testament times John the Baptist apparently found no hardship in his diet of "locusts and wild honey" (Matt. 3:4; Mark 1:6).

The Moth

Many of the insects mentioned in the Bible are either pests or outright menaces; the moth is one of these. People of biblical times, from the days of the prophets to the days of Jesus, had at least one thing in common with us, in so far as daily housekeeping problems were concerned—how to keep moths away from clothing. And, to our knowledge, in those days no one had yet invented mothballs.

As is the case with many other insects and animals, the whole family of moths bears the stigma of just a couple of its members. There are countless moths that have no interest in feeding on wool, fur, or any other fabric—these we notice only as phantom-like creatures attracted to flame, or any form of light. The two culprits are known as the case-making clothes moth and the webbing clothes moth, and even they are destructive only in the larval stage, and not after they have reached maturity. It is no use, as many have discovered to their dismay, to kill the winged creature that flutters from the closet or dresser drawer; the damage has already been done.

The moth reproduces in May or June. Moths enter human

CLASSIFICATION. *Tinea pellionella* (case-making clothes moth) and *Tineola biselliella* (webbing clothes moth), members of Tineidae family of order Lepidoptera (butterflies and moths).

LEXICON. *Hebrew:* ASH. *Greek:* SES.

Joining a bird in flight is this outsized moth, as seen by an Egyptian wall-painter of the Eighteenth Dynasty (fourteenth century B.C.). Perhaps the artist was impressed with the moth's ability to destroy and thus added to his size; more likely, however, he was attracted to the pattern and coloration of the delicate wings. (Photograph courtesy of the Oriental Institute of the University of Chicago.)

dwellings in the evening, and while the male flies dauntlessly around and becomes the object of violent and dramatic moth hunts, the female quietly finds her way to where the clothes are kept, there to lay her eggs in their midst. A week later the larvae appear and immediately begin their work of destruction (although to them it is simply a matter of staying alive), eating anything within reach that is made of animal fibers.

THE SECRET SPOILER

The hallmark of the moth's destructive activity is that it is done in secret, without any buzzing, without any dramatic appearance in a swarm that blots out the sun. But biblical writers were quite aware of its danger, and the Hebrew name for the insect, *ash*, means "the spoiler." In an age when wealth was counted more in possessions than in money, and highly valued among possessions was wool clothing (see "The Sheep"), moths could literally cause economic disaster. Thus the words of Jesus in the Sermon on the Mount take on added emphasis: "Do not lay up for yourselves treasures on earth, where moth and rust consume" (Matt. 6:19). The same saying is put a slightly different way in Luke: "Provide yourselves with purses that do not grow old, with a treasure in the heavens that does not fail, where no thief approaches and no moth destroys" (Luke 12:33). The meaning could not be more clear: the thought of moth-eaten clothing impressed on Jesus' listeners the transitoriness of human wealth. James uses the same language later in his epistle: "Your riches have rotted and your garments are moth-eaten" (Jas. 5:2). And a psalmist had much earlier used a similar figure of speech: "When thou dost chasten man with rebukes for sin, thou dost consume like a moth what is dear to him" (Ps. 39:11).

LIKE A MOTH

Many biblical writers employed a fact of everyday life in a figurative manner, in order to give their messages poetic impact. Thus for the prophet Hosea moths could become a metaphor for the annihilating wrath of the Lord: "Therefore [says the Lord] I am like a moth to Ephraim, and like dry rot to the house of Judah" (Hos. 5:12). The enemies of the Lord will suffer the same fate as a piece of moth-ridden clothing, according to Isaiah: "Behold, all of them will wear out like a garment; the moth will eat them up" (Isa. 50:9). But the most striking use of the moth in relation to human life is found in Job, in the speech during which Job calls God to account and bitterly describes the human condition: "Man wastes away like a rotten thing, like a garment that is moth-eaten" (Job 13:28).

The Scorpion

Neither the scorpion nor its relative the spider are insects, that is, members of the class Insecta, but both are included in this section because they are more closely related to the insects than to any of the creatures treated in the final section of the book. Both are arachnids, that is, members of the class Arachnida. They are at least distant relatives of the insects, for Insecta and Arachnida are major divisions in the phylum Arthropoda (animals with segmented bodies and limbs).

MYSTERIOUS SURVIVOR

Throughout the ages the scorpion has been surrounded by an aura of horror and mystery, and in fact it is a survivor of the age of dinosaurs, a so-called living fossil. It prefers the warmer climates (perhaps because it has survived an ice age or two) and thus is quite common in the Holy Land. Because of its desire for warmth, the scorpion has the disconcerting habit of entering houses, especially at night, and hiding in beds, blankets, footwear, and clothing. It is especially

---

CLASSIFICATION. Some species of order Scorpionida of Arachnida class of phylum Arthropoda.

LEXICON. *Hebrew:* AQRAB. *Greek:* SKORPIOS.

disconcerting since the sting of a scorpion is extremely painful and occasionally fatal to human beings.

One of the more common species of scorpion found in Palestine is the rock scorpion, larger and more dangerous than most. It is as thick as a man's finger and from five to seven inches in length, with eight eyes and four pairs of legs. Both the upper and lower jaws have pincers that are used to hold and cut up the scorpion's prey, and the lower pincers are especially large and terrifying. The rear of the body terminates in a long "tail," consisting of six narrowing body joints curling up and forward over the creature's head. It is at the tip of this "tail" that the scorpion's poison sting is located, which it uses to paralyze its prey while holding it with the pincers.

The scorpion will not maliciously attack a human being,

Looking like a fossil embedded in rock, this scorpion is actually part of a carved limestone plaque from late dynastic Egypt. Note the artist's biological accuracy. The hieroglyphic writing on the stone spells out an incantation against evil. (Photograph courtesy of the Metropolitan Museum of Art; Dodge Fund, 1947.)

but it will defend itself with great vigor if disturbed. It feeds on insects and spiders, hunting them at night. When it has caught its victim after a rapid chase, it holds it firmly with its pincers, examines it carefully, and then, if it decides that the victim is edible, stings it and sucks out the body juices. In many species the female scorpion dispatches the male after mating has taken place. It used to be believed that the scorpion bore its young alive, but actually it lays eggs that hatch in a very short time. During the early part of their lives young scorpions live on their mother's body, and since they are numerous and quite active a scorpion with its young is a very strange sight.

SCORPIONS IN WILDERNESS

People in biblical times were no less impressed by the scorpion than people today. The travails of the Israelites during the Exodus included scorpions; the land they traveled through was described as "the great and terrible wilderness, with its fiery serpents and scorpions and thirsty ground where there was no water" (Deut. 8:15). The scorpion was frequently regarded as an instrument of God's punishment; the author of the apocryphal Ecclesiastus says: "The teeth of wild beasts, and scorpions and vipers, and the sword that punishes the ungodly with destruction; they will rejoice in his commands, and be made ready on earth for their service" (Ecclus. 39:30-31). The same writer, however, offers us this wry comment on the matrimonial situation: "An evil wife is an ox yoke which chafes; taking hold of her is like grasping a scorpion" (Ecclus. 26:7).

COMPARED TO REBELLIOUS PEOPLE

The book of Ezekiel also makes figurative use of the scorpion, in this case comparing it to the rebellious people of Israel, who will not welcome God's representative, the son of man (that is, Ezekiel), with open arms: "And you, son of man, be not afraid of them, nor be afraid of their words, though briers and thorns are with you and you sit upon scorpions; be not afraid of their words, nor be dismayed at their looks, for they are a rebellious house" (Ezek. 2:6). It is the Lord who is speaking here, appointing Ezekiel to be his prophet, and He is certainly not allowing him to go forth with any illusions about the job. Another figurative use of the scorpion involves an instrument of torture, the scourge, which apparently was intended to feel, and undoubtedly did, like the sting of a scorpion: "My father chastised you with whips, but I will chastise you with scorpions" (I Kings 12:11, 14; II Chron. 10:11, 14).

JESUS KNEW

Jesus, whose words so often reveal an intimate acquaintance with nature, was no stranger to the scorpion. In the course of his teaching, he asks: "What father among you, if his son . . . asks for an egg, will give him a scorpion?" (Luke 11:11-12). A coiled rock scorpion might bear a certain resemblance to an egg, but what is really being stressed here is the complete trust that a young child has in his father. When he sent his disciples out on their first preaching mission, Jesus was well aware of the danger they were facing, but bolstered them with these words: "Behold, I have given you authority to tread upon serpents and scorpions, and over all the power of the enemy; and nothing shall hurt you" (Luke 10:19).

Not surprisingly, the scorpion plays a part in the picture of the last days that is conjured up in the book of Revelation. When the bottomless pit is opened, smoke arises and "from the smoke came locusts on the earth, and they were given power like the power of scorpions of the earth. . . . And their torture was like the torture of a scorpion, when it stings a man" (Rev. 9:3, 5).

229

The Spider

The spider is one of those creatures that has captured the imagination of human beings from the earliest times, not because it is particularly attractive, but because of what it does. The spider's web, which it constructs from a fluid in its body, fascinates us. A Greek myth sought to explain the spider web in supernatural terms; in it, a beautiful young woman named Arachne is such a skilled weaver that she challenges the goddess of wisdom and the arts, Pallas Athene, to a weaving contest. Her arrogance has led her to bite off more than she can chew, however, and the goddess metes out a fitting punishment: Arachne is transformed into a squat, ugly creature who must spin silk out of her own body. Apparently she is allowed to retain her skills, for the spider web remains one of the most beautiful objects known to man. Scientists later drew upon the myth to find a name for the class of creatures of which the spider is a representative, the Arachnida.

FRAGILITY OF WEB

In the Bible, however, it is not the beauty of the spider web that is stressed, but its fragility. To the few biblical authors that took note of the spider at all, its web represented the transitory or flimsy. Thus, in the book of Job: "His con-

---

CLASSIFICATION. Some species of order Araneida of Arachnida class of phylum Arthropoda.
LEXICON. *Hebrew:* AKKABISH.

The delicate patterns of a spider web are seen in this photograph, which also reveals why biblical writers considered it flimsy. To an insect caught in it, however, it is anything but fragile. (Photograph courtesy of Ewing Galloway.)

231

fidence breaks in sunder, and his trust is a spider's web"—such is the lot of the godless man, according to Job's "comforter," Bildad the Shuhite (Job 8:14). Later, Job too philosophizes upon the fate of the wicked man: "The house which he builds is like a spider's web. . . . The east wind lifts him up and he is gone; it sweeps him out of his place" (Job 27:18, 21). In listing the offenses and shortcomings of the Israelites, Isaiah tells us scornfully that "they weave the spider's web" and that "their webs will not serve as clothing" (Isa. 59: 5, 6). Here the web symbolizes something evil, for the prophet goes on to explain: "Men will not cover themselves with what they make. Their works are works of iniquity, and deeds of violence are in their hands" (Isa. 59:6).

Nevertheless, the spinning of a spider web remains a wondrous thing, and of course it is of prime importance to the spider itself. The male constructs a net for use during the mating season; the female weaves another to hide and protect her eggs, and lines her winter quarters with the same thread used in the web. Mainly, though, the spider uses its spinning prowess to catch its food, producing the intricate patterns we admire for the mundane purpose of snaring insects in their sticky threads. And, in spite of the attitude found in Job and Isaiah, the thread produced by the spider is amazingly strong considering that the finest ones have a diameter of as little as 1/3600 of an inch.

SPECIES UNKNOWN

Hundreds of species of spiders are found in Palestine, making it useless to single out one as being most familiar to biblical writers. Some species are poisonous, but none of these has ever achieved the notoriety of the black widow or the tarantula, nor did they impress biblical writers sufficiently to be mentioned in the same manner as the scorpion (q.v.).

Mollusks,
Fish,
Reptiles,
and
Worms

The Crocodile

Although one will not find the crocodile by name in either of the most widely used English versions of the Bible, a lengthy passage in the book of Job describes this reptile in detail: "I will not keep silence concerning his limbs, or his mighty strength, or his goodly frame. Who can strip off his outer garment? Who can penetrate his double coat of mail? Who can open the doors of his face? Round about his teeth is terror. His back is made of rows of shields, shut up closely as with a seal. One is so near to another that no air can come between them. They are joined one to another; they clasp each other and cannot be separated. . . . In his neck abides strength, and terror dances before him. The folds of his flesh cleave together, firmly cast upon him and immovable. His heart is hard as a stone, hard as the nether millstone. . . . His underparts are like sharp potsherds; he spreads himself like a threshing sledge on the mire. He makes the deep boil like a pot; he makes the sea like a pot of ointment" (Job 41:12-17, 22-24, 30-31).

It is possible, of course, that the beast here described is mythical, in which case the English versions are safe in call-

---

CLASSIFICATION. *Crocodilus niloticus* (Egyptian crocodile), member of Crocodilidae family of order Crocodilia (comprising only twenty-four species of crocodile and alligator) of Reptilia class of the vertebrates. LEXICON. *Hebrew:* LIVYATHAN.

---

ing it "Leviathan," which is simply a transliteration of the Hebrew word *livyathan*. But the author of Job shows himself elsewhere to be a careful observer of nature, and though his language is indeed poetic, the description can very easily be seen to fit the crocodile.

COULD AUTHOR HAVE SEEN?

There is still some question as to whether or not the writer of Job, a native of Palestine, would actually have had an opportunity to observe the crocodile, since it is not found in that country today. It is, and has been throughout recorded history, a native of the Nile Valley; in fact, one usually thinks of the Nile in connection with the crocodile, and the variety there is called the "Nile crocodile" both commonly and in scientific terms (*Crocodilus niloticus*). Although rarely encountered as far north as Egypt nowadays, in ancient times it was very common there. In addition, certain evidence supports the theory that it was also to be found in Palestine. The Roman historian Pliny refers to a place in Palestine called Crocodeilopolis ("crocodile city"), to the south of Mount Carmel; and explorers in the Holy Land as late as the nineteenth century reported seeing crocodiles in the same general region.

OBSERVED FEROCITY

Thus it would seem that the author of Job had opportunity to observe the crocodile, whether or not he ever visited Egypt. He has further things to say about the crocodile: "Can you draw out Leviathan with a fishhook, or press down his tongue with a cord? Can you put a rope in his nose, or pierce his jaw with a hook? Will he make many supplications to you? Will he speak to you soft words? Will he make a covenant with you to take him for your servant for ever? Will you play with him as with a bird, or will you put him on leash for your maidens? Will traders bargain over him? Will they

This Egyptian manuscript of the Ptolemaic period (323-30 B.C.) shows a trio of crocodiles in flight from a hunter armed with a spear, a highly unlikely sight considering the nature of the reptile. (Photograph courtesy of the Metropolitan Museum of Art; gift of Edward S. Harkness, 1935.)

divide him up among the merchants? Can you fill his skin with harpoons, or his head with fishing spears? Lay hands on him; think of the battle; you will not do it again!" (Job 41:1-8).

Here the author is preoccupied with the ferocity of the crocodile, but there are obvious references to the difficulties encountered when hunting or trapping the creature. We know from archeological research that this reptile was indeed hunted by the ancient Egyptians, who sometimes kept it in captivity. They considered it a holy creature, one of the assistants of the god Osiris.

STIRRED IMAGINATION

It is not strange that an animal with the fantastic appearance, the enormous strength, and the fearless nature of the crocodile stirred the imaginations of people in ancient times. The author of Job was struck by its "double coat of mail," armor which consists of hard plates of bone embedded in its leathery skin. These are actually scales, like those found on almost all of the reptiles, but proportionately larger since the crocodile reaches a length of eighteen feet. "Round about his teeth is terror," and such fear is by no means groundless,

With a flair for correct proportions and realism, an Egyptian artist sculptured this crocodile from bronze. Note the flat, strong tail with which the reptile propels itself through the water. (Photograph courtesy of the Oriental Institute of the University of Chicago.)

for the large mouth of the crocodile is equipped with about seventy teeth of varying sizes irregularly placed—a formidable hunting weapon. Its head is so constructed that in the water it can approach its victim with only its nostrils showing above the surface. The dirty green color of its scales and its general shape also make it difficult to distinguish from a floating log; all in all one can understand why the author of Job speaks of the crocodile with awe.

"THE MIGHTY ARE AFRAID"

Thus it is that "the mighty are afraid; at the crashing they are beside themselves. Though the sword reaches him, it does not avail; nor the spear, the dart, or the javelin. He counts iron as straw, and bronze as rotten wood. The arrow cannot make him flee; for him slingstones are turned to stubble. Clubs are counted as stubble; he laughs at the rattle of javelins" (Job 41:25-29). The sight of a crocodile whipping the water into foam with his long bladelike tail is both picturesque and awe-inspiring: "He makes the deep boil like a pot; he makes the sea like a pot of ointment" (Job 41:31). "Ointment" may refer to the pronounced odor of musk that the crocodile exudes from two glands situated on its lower jaw. These musk glands are actually used in the manufacture of perfume, making the hunting of crocodiles a fairly prosperous business. The flesh is a popular food among Africans, but is usually shunned by Europeans and other non-Africans because of its musky smell.

FISH-EATER

The crocodile spends most of its time in the water, where it feeds mainly on fish, but also on aquatic birds and even small mammals that come down to the water's edge to drink. It is surprisingly fast and agile on dry land, however, even though its legs are so short that its belly and tail drag across the earth leaving a distinct path. Thus the observation: "His underparts are like sharp potsherds; he spreads himself like a threshing sledge on the mire" (Job 41:30). Crocodiles, in spite of many jungle movies to the contrary, attack human beings only in self-defense or when they think they are threatened.

MYTHICAL DRAGON

Other portions of the Bible make reference to the Leviathan, but in all of these instances it would seem probable that the writers did not have the crocodile in mind, but some imaginary or mythological creature. It appears as a playful sea monster in one place (Ps. 104:26), as a serpentine creature fleeing the wrath of the Lord in Isaiah (27:1), and possibly as a dragon of some kind in another psalm (74:14). In any case, few living creatures possess more characteristics of the unearthly than the crocodile, and certainly no extant animal bears a closer resemblance to the traditional picture of the mythological dragon.

The Fish

Among the many references to fish in both the Old and New Testaments there is not a single mention of any special kind, with the possible exception of the famous fish that swallowed Jonah (see "The 'Great Fish'"). Otherwise the only distinction made is between fish that are clean and those that are unclean in the Mosaic law: "These you may eat, of all that are in the waters. Everything in the waters that has fins and scales, whether in the seas or in the rivers, you may eat. But anything in the seas or the rivers that has not fins and scales, of the swarming creatures in the waters and of the living creatures that are in the waters, is an abomination to you" (Lev. 11:9-10).

Even here, it will be noted, the Bible does not use the word "fish," and as we have seen in the case of the banned sea cow (q.v.), not all the creatures that live in the water are fish, that is, members of the Pisces class of vertebrates. Therefore the only *fish* native to the Mediterranean or local lakes that

---

CLASSIFICATION. Cichlidae family (perches) of order Percomorphi; Cyprinidae family (carp and barbels) and Siluridae family (ca⁺fish) of order Ostariophysi; both orders of Pisces class of the vertebrates.

LEXICON. *Hebrew:* DAG, DAGAH. *Greek:* ICHTHUS, ICHTHUDION. Also, OPSARION (little fish).

were banned from Israelites' tables were catfish (the Siluridae family) and eels (order Apodes), since these lack scales. Other fishlike creatures coming under the ban would be rays, lampreys, and sharks, commonly called fishes but belonging to other zoological classes of vertebrates.

FRESH-WATER FISH

In any case, the fish allowed to be eaten under the dietary laws were a popular food among the Israelites, especially after they were settled in Palestine. Since the people of Israel were never a seafaring nation, it is safe to assume that most of their fish came from fresh-water lakes and rivers, especially the Sea of Galilee. Some thirty-six species of fish have been identified by modern zoologists in that large lake, including varieties of perch, carp, barbels, "sardines," and the forbidden catfish. The Jewish historian Josephus, who lived in New Testament times, made the following observations about the Sea of Galilee: "The sea has fresh water that is very pleasant to drink; the water flows freely and is not muddy like in swamps. The water is clear, for the sea has sandy beaches everywhere. . . . In the sea there are species of fish that with regard to both taste and appearance are different from those found anywhere else" (*The Jewish Wars*, III, Book X, 7). Whether or not this claim was correct, we have no way of knowing which fish Josephus meant.

NEW TESTAMENT INDUSTRY

Since fish was such a highly-favored food, and since only relatively few residents of Palestine had access to the Sea of Galilee, fishing was an important industry, especially in New Testament times. This is not to say that the eating of fish was uncommon in Old Testament times, for we have the dietary laws as evidence to the contrary, as well as such references as the Israelites' complaint during their wilderness sojourn: "We remember the fish we ate in Egypt for nothing" (Num.

11:5). The Fish Gate of Jerusalem, so named apparently because fish were sold there, is mentioned in II Chron. 33:14; Neh. 3:3; 12:39; and Zeph. 1:10. But readers of the New Testament are particularly aware of the part fish played in the lives of Jesus' contemporaries, primarily because several of the disciples were fishermen by profession. In one well-known instance Jesus preached to people along the shore of the Sea of Galilee while he himself was sitting in a fishing boat near shore (Matt. 13:2).

Jesus, whose home town of Nazareth was only a short distance from the Sea of Galilee, drew his earliest followers—

Fishing is an ancient industry, as can be seen from this Egyptian wall painting of about 1450 B.C. The man on the left is slitting open a fish before salt-curing it. Perhaps it was such fish as these that the Israelites in the wilderness claimed they got "for nothing" in Egypt. (Photograph courtesy of the Metropolitan Museum of Art.)

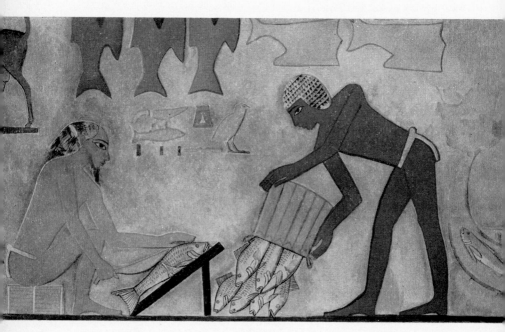

Simon Peter and his brother Andrew, and James and John the sons of Zebedee—from that profession, charging them to be forthwith "fishers of men" (Matt. 4:18-22). As many Christians have found out throughout the ages, it is no easy task to be a "fisher of men," but the life of a fisherman in New Testament times was not easy either, and perhaps prepared the four disciples for the rugged life ahead.

DRAGNET

Several methods of fishing were in use in New Testament times, but that most favored by commercial fishermen such as Peter and Andrew was the dragnet. After a boat had "put out into the deep" (Luke 5:4), a large net would be thrown out from it and then dragged toward the shore by the rowers in the boat, possibly with the help of another crew in another boat. The catch would then be sorted out on the shore (Matt. 13:47-48). Such fishing was carried on at night, when the coolness of the water brought the fish closer to the surface and when they could not see the approaching nets. This explains Peter's surprise when Jesus told him to put out his nets in the middle of the day, after "we toiled all night and took nothing" (Luke 5:5). Nevertheless, he obeyed: "But at your word I will let down the nets." As the reader of the Bible knows, the catch was so great that the two boats working at the time nearly foundered. It is no wonder that the seasoned fisherman Peter "was astonished, and all that were with him" (Luke 5:9).

HOOK AND LINE

The other methods used were the simple hook and line— the common method known to sportsmen in our day—the spear (mentioned only in Job 41:7, 26), and the thrownet, which is rarely used nowadays except in primitive cultures. The New Testament reference to fishing with a hook occurs in Jesus' discussion of the temple tax with Peter. Jesus feels no obligation to pay the tax, but in order not to give unnecessary offense, he tells Peter to "go to the sea and cast a hook, and take the first fish that comes up, and when you open its mouth you will find a shekel; take that and give it to them for me and for yourself" (Matt. 17:27). We are not told whether Peter followed these instructions to the letter, but presumably any good fisherman would be able to employ any of several methods of fishing. The thrownet, mentioned in Ezek. 47:10, was undoubtedly popular among some of the less prosperous people living along the shores of Galilee. It was a circular net that could be handled by one man who would wade out from the shore, cast the net out into the sea as far as possible, and then haul in whatever he might snare.

BOILED, STEAMED, SALTED

Once the fish was caught it could be prepared in a number of ways, just as in our own time—by boiling, steaming, frying, pickling, or salting. Salt-curing was probably the most common method of preserving fish that were to be shipped any distance or kept for any length of time; it was probably this kind of fish that was involved in the feeding of the five thousand (Luke 9:10-17). Jesus himself undoubtedly enjoyed eating fish: on several occasions he shared such a meal with his disciples (for example, Luke 24:42-43; John 21:13).

JESUS' EXAMPLES

Jesus spoke to people in language they could understand and appreciate, and so when he preached to the people who lived along the shores of the Sea of Galilee, he frequently drew examples from the life of the fisherman. Once he explained to his disciples: "Again, the kingdom of heaven is like a net which was thrown into the sea and gathered fish of every kind; when it was full, men drew it ashore and sat down and sorted the good into vessels but threw away the bad. So it will be at the close of the age" (Matt. 13:47-49). In the Sermon on the Mount Jesus asked rhetorically: "What

"Cast the net on the right side of the boat," Jesus tells Peter and the other disciples (John 21:6). This appearance of the risen Christ on the shores of Galilee appears in a Byzantine mosaic at S. Apollinare Nuovo, Ravenna. (Photograph courtesy of the Metropolitan Museum of Art; Johnson Fund, 1924.)

245

man of you, if his son asks him for a loaf, will give him a stone? Or if he asks for a fish, will give him a serpent?" (Matt. 7:9-10). The choice of a serpent seems strange, but it is possible that Jesus had in mind the snakes that even today are found in great numbers along the shore of the Sea of Galilee and frequently take the hooks of fishermen or show up in their nets. Or perhaps the reference is to the eel, which was considered unclean.

Very early in the history of the Christian church the fish became a symbol for Christ. It was scratched onto the walls of the Roman catacombs, and today may be seen decorating walls, altars, pews, and vestments in many churches. This symbol came into use because the Greek word for fish, *ichthus*, is composed of the first letters of the Greek phrase for "Jesus Christ, Son of God, Savior," *Iesous CHristos THeou Uios Soter.*

Far to the east of Palestine, near Ur, the original home of Abraham, this fish was modeled out of terra cotta, probably in the third millennium B.C. During the Babylonian reign in the same area, a thousand years later, the water god Ea, half man and half fish, was worshiped. (Photograph courtesy of the University Museum, Philadelphia.)

The Frog

"Then the Lord said to Moses, 'Go in to Pharaoh and say to him, "Thus says the Lord, 'Let my people go, that they may serve me. But if you refuse to let them go, behold, I will plague all your country with frogs; the Nile shall swarm with frogs which shall come up into your house, and into your bed-chamber and on your bed, and into the houses of your servants and of your people, and into your ovens and your kneading bowls; the frogs shall come up on you and on your people and on all your servants.'"' And the Lord said to Moses, 'Say to Aaron, "Stretch out your hand with your rod over the rivers, over the canals, and over the pools, and cause frogs to come upon the land of Egypt!"' So Aaron stretched out his hand over the waters of Egypt; and the frogs came up and covered the land of Egypt" (Exod. 8:1-6).

ONLY INTRUSION

Except for two references to the same event in the Psalms ("Their land swarmed with frogs, even in the chambers of their kings" Ps. 105:30; cf. Ps. 78:45) and one poetic reference in the book of Revelation, this story represents the only

---

CLASSIFICATION. *Chiromantis, Polypedates,* and allied genera (tree frogs), members of Ranidae family (frogs) of order Ecaudata (tailless amphibians) of Amphibia class of the vertebrates.

LEXICON. *Hebrew:* TSEPHARDEA. *Greek:* BATRACHOS.

intrusion of the frog, indeed of the entire class of amphibians, into biblical narrative. The frog seems to have been one of those creatures that, although fairly common in parts of the Near East, did not attract much attention, either favorable or unfavorable, from the Israelites. The Egyptians, however, who seemed to have a place for every animal native to their country among their many gods, associated the frog with the goddess Heqet, who assisted women in childbirth.

SWARMED OVER LAND

There is little doubt, then, that the frogs which invaded the land during the second plague were already native to Egypt, and their coming up out of the river and the marshy areas can be viewed as a consequence of the water having been polluted by the first plague (see "The Gnat" and "The Fly"). There is no way of determining what variety of frog it was, if indeed it was only one. Many species are found in the swamps of Egypt today. One might narrow the field to the tree frog, which is not much help, for there are two hundred seventy species of this frog, many of which are native to Egypt. Tree frogs are distinguished by the adhesive pads at the tips of their toes that enable them to climb even smooth vertical walls, let alone trees. Like all amphibians they begin their life cycle in the water, and large hordes of tree frogs have been known to suddenly leave their breeding grounds and swarm across the surrounding countryside.

Of course, unlike the other creatures involved in the plagues, frogs are not especially harmful to human beings, and it is their "nuisance" value that is emphasized in the Exodus story. But people always have associated them with sliminess and foulness, as is done in the book of Revelation. Here John declares that he saw in his vision "issuing from the mouth of the dragon and from the mouth of the beast and from the mouth of the false prophet, three foul spirits like frogs" (Rev. 16:13).

The "Great Fish"

"And the Lord appointed a great fish to swallow up Jonah; and Jonah was in the belly of the fish three days and three nights" (Jonah 1:17). There is no other comment in the well-known story of Jonah about the "great fish" except that eventually "it vomited out Jonah upon the dry land" (Jonah 2:10). Because people of the past could imagine no larger "fish" than a whale, this story is known traditionally as "Jonah and the Whale."

We know today, however, that the whale is not a fish but a mammal, and whether or not the biblical author was aware of this fact, it is also a fact that no species of whale has an esophagus large enough for a man to pass through. Also, whales are quite rare in the Mediterranean Sea, where the event took place. The Hebrew gives us no help in identifying the creature, since the words used here are general terms for "fish" and "large." It is possible then that the biblical writer had in mind the shark, probably the great white shark, which

---

CLASSIFICATION. Some species of genus *Carcharodon* (great white sharks), members of Lamnidae family of order Pleurotremi (sharks) of Selachii class of the vertebrates.

LEXICON. *Hebrew:* DAG modified by GADOL.

lives in the Mediterranean. It sometimes reaches a length of forty feet, and is capable of swallowing a man whole.

The shark is not, strictly speaking, a fish—that is, a member of the Pisces class of aquatic vertebrates. Rather, it is a selachian, belonging to the same class as the dogfish and rays. The great white shark is noted as a man-eater, although instances of sharks attacking humans are much less frequent than is popularly supposed.

It is pure conjecture, of course, to identify the "great fish" as a shark, but it seems to be the best possibility. Any such identification cannot take away from the story's main point: it was the Lord who directed Jonah's destiny by causing the

A medieval illuminator had his own ideas of what the "great fish" that swallowed Jonah looked like, as can be seen in this initial from a fourteenth-century Latin Bible. (Photograph courtesy of the Pierpont Morgan Library.)

fish to be on hand to swallow Jonah when he was tossed overboard and by keeping him alive inside the fish for three days and three nights. Even if a man inside a shark's belly could somehow obtain air, it would do him no good, for under ordinary circumstances the shark's strong digestive juices would complete the job that the shark's sharp teeth had neglected to do.

The Leech

The only true worm mentioned in the Bible (see "The Fly") is the leech, and it appears only once. Even then, the passage in which it appears, in the book of Proverbs, is not among the most lucid in the Bible: "The leech has two daughters; 'Give, give,' they cry" (Prov. 30:15). A person can be called a "leech" in modern American slang, and here in Proverbs the reference apparently is also to the parasitic and greedy nature of the leech, for this verse is followed immediately by: "Three things are never satisfied; four never say, 'Enough': Sheol, the barren womb, the earth ever thirsty for water, and the fire which never says, 'Enough'" (Prov. 30:15-16). The "two daughters" are possibly symbols for man's sensuality and avarice.

As far as human beings are concerned, the leech is one of

CLASSIFICATION. *Limnatis nilotica* ("horse leech"), member of Hirudidae family of order Gnathobdellae of Hirudinea class (leeches) of phylum Annelida (segmented worms).
LEXICON. *Hebrew:* ALUQAH.

the more unpleasant of the thousands and thousands of parasitic animals, since it is one of the relatively few that draws its sustenance from man. It is a segmented worm of from one to five inches in length, with a flat body that is equipped with suction pads at each end which are used for locomotion. The mouth, located at the bottom of the front suction pad, has three sharp knifelike projections with which the leech pierces the skin of its host. It feeds on blood, and possesses glands that secrete an anticoagulant to prevent the blood from clotting.

One species of leech was for many centuries employed in the service of the healing arts, when bloodletting was considered beneficial in certain ailments. This practice was most popular in the nineteenth century; today it is considered to be either harmful or useless. There is no evidence that the leech was used in this manner during biblical times, at least not in the area of Palestine.

GOOD GUESS

As in similar cases where an animal is mentioned only once in the Bible, it is impossible to identify the creature in question except in the most general zoological terms. The largest local species in Palestine, sometimes called the "horse leech" (as in the KJV), is as good a guess as any. It is particularly insidious since it enters its host's mouth or nostrils from water while the animal is drinking. As its name implies, however, it is more attracted to horses than to humans.

The Lizards

Wherever the countryside is parched and barren, there lizards are most likely to be found. In the Near East they are thus encountered in the greatest numbers in the Arabian desert, the Sinai peninsula, and the Judean wilderness. Despite that they were familiar creatures, these reptiles are mentioned only once apart from the dietary laws given to the Israelites during their long stay in the Sinai wilderness. Forbidden as food were "the great lizard according to its kind, the gecko, the land crocodile, the lizard, the sand lizard, and the chameleon" (Lev. 11:29-30). The names used in the RSV are rather arbitrary, but it is almost certain that all of the creatures named here are lizards.

Apparently the Hebrew word translated as "lizard" in both the KJV and the RSV should be taken to mean simply lizards in general, although it is curious that it would be included with names of specific varieties. The RSV is probably correct in its rendering of one of these names as the "gecko" ("ferret" in the KJV). Geckoes, that is, members of the Geckonidae family, are nocturnal hunters that feed on insects and spiders

---

CLASSIFICATION. *Uromastix spinipes* ("great lizard"), member of Agamidae family; Geckonidae family (geckoes); *Midrosaurus niloticus* (Nile monitor), member of Varanidae family; Scincidae family (skinks); all of suborder Lacertilia; suborder Rheptoglossa (chameleons); both of Reptilia class of the vertebrates.

LEXICON. *Hebrew:* LETAAH (lizard); ANAQAH (gecko); KOACH (monitor); TINSHEMETH (chameleon); TSAB (agamid); CHOMET (skink).

and are equipped with suction pads on their feet that enable them to climb smooth surfaces. Their scaly skin is dark and seems to be covered with warts. Ordinarily they move slowly and hesitantly, but they are capable of great speed when frightened.

AGAMID AND MONITOR

The "great lizard" of the RSV ("tortoise" in the KJV) is probably an agamid, specifically the species known only by its scientific name *Uromastix spinipes*. This large lizard, which grows to be three feet long, has a sinister appearance, for it is covered with sharp scales and thorny protrusions; actually, it is harmless and even timid, living on beetles and other insects. The "land crocodile" ("chameleon" in the KJV) might well be a monitor lizard. The varieties found in Palestine are also about three feet long, and are sand-colored creatures with yellow-green spots on their bodies and golden rings on their necks; they prey on insects, snails, frogs, and mice. In Egypt is found the Nile monitor, which may grow to twice the size of the Palestinian species and is of a darker color. This animal eats smaller lizards and tortoises, baby crocodiles, and small birds and mammals.

CHAMELEON

The RSV is possibly correct in its choice of "chameleon" for another Hebrew word on the list ("mole" in the KJV). The Palestinian varieties are from eight to twelve inches long, but otherwise share the characteristics of the species with which we are familiar. Their large protruding eyes move independently of one another and enable them to follow the movements of their prey, usually insects, without moving their own bodies. Like frogs, they have long, sticky tongues that shoot out four to six inches to catch a fly. They are known for their ability to change color, not, as is sometimes believed, for self-protection, but as an involuntary response apparently

Although few lizards are more than three feet long, and most are less than a foot long, they look like the great reptiles that roamed the earth in prehistoric times. Shown here are four of the lizards prohibited by the dietary laws in Leviticus: the agamid (top), the chameleon (left center), the gecko (right center), and the Nile monitor. (Drawing by Carol Wilde.)

255

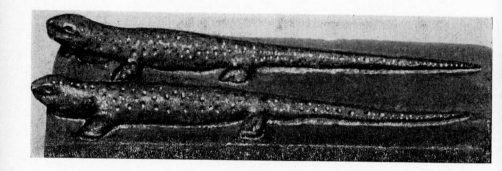

This pair of bronze lizards (perhaps geckoes) was sculptured in ancient Egypt, in the same style and perhaps by the same artist who created the crocodile shown on page 238. (Photograph courtesy of the Oriental Institute of the University of Chicago.)

connected with their emotions. Finally there is the RSV's "sand lizard" ("snail" in the KJV), which may refer to any one of a variety of skinks found in Palestine.

INCONSPICUOUS, YET WISE

The one mention of the lizard outside of the dietary laws occurs in the RSV translation of Proverbs, where the lizard is listed with the ant, the rock badger, and the locust (q.v.) as a creature that is inconspicuous and yet has wisdom: "The lizard you can take in your hands, yet it is in king's palaces" (Prov. 30:28). But the context here would seem to support the KJV rendering of the Hebrew word in question as "spider," for few lizards are especially inconspicuous and, although geckoes are occasionally seen in houses, most lizards prefer the open spaces of the wilderness.

The Pearl Oyster

From the earliest times the pearl has been regarded as a valuable and noble ornament, and the Greeks and Romans considered perfect pearls to be among the most valuable of all jewels. The pearl is not, of course, a mineral like most gems, but an abnormal growth that develops within a mollusk when a grain of sand or some other foreign body becomes lodged between the mollusk's shell and its mantle (the fold or lobe of its body wall which lines the shell). The mollusk is irritated by the foreign matter, but is unable to get rid of it; so it protects itself by covering the foreign body with layers of the same calcic substance that is on the inside of its shell.

THE PEARL FORMS

Eventually the pearl we know is formed, a smooth, nacreous body, not attached to either the shell or the mollusk's body; it may be round, shaped like a teardrop, or irregular. Its color may be milky white, yellowish, rose, purple, or black. From one to a hundred pearls may be found within a single mollusk, varying in size from pearls as small as poppy seeds to ones

---

CLASSIFICATION. *Pinctada margaritifera* (pearl oyster found in Red Sea), member of order Filibranchia of Lemellibranchia class of phylum Mollusca.

LEXICON. *Hebrew:* GABISH. Also, DAR (mother-of-pearl). *Greek:* MARGARITES.

257

as large as cherries and even, in very rare cases, as large as a pigeon's egg.

All mollusks that have shells can produce pearls, but it is the bivalve known as the pearl oyster that produces the most valuable pearls and is thus the foundation of the pearl industry. It is found on extensive underwater banks in the Red Sea, the Persian Gulf, and the Indian Ocean, especially near Ceylon where the finest specimens are found. Like all oysters, the pearl oyster attaches itself to the ocean floor. Pearl divers who have trained themselves to stay underwater for long periods of time collect these mollusks, which vary in diameter from two to twelve inches. The shells are then separated with a knife and examined for pearls. It is estimated that one salable pearl, that is, one large enough to be of commercial value, is found in every one hundred oysters examined—which explains their relatively high price today and in ancient times.

IN JOB FIRST

As in most civilizations in world history, ancient Near Easterners valued the pearl highly, and only royalty or the well-to-do could afford to own them. But they seem not to have been known to the Israelites until fairly late in their history, since the first mention of a pearl is in the book of Job. By the time of the New Testament they were well known to biblical writers as a prized commodity that only the rich could afford.

WORN BY HARLOTS

This category would include the harlot and the courtesan, and among other valuables, the harlot of Babylon in the book of Revelation possesses them: "The woman was arrayed in purple and scarlet, and bedecked with gold and jewels and pearls" (Rev. 17:4). In the epistle to Timothy Christian women are warned to shun such luxuries; they should "adorn themselves modestly and sensibly in seemly apparel, not with braided hair or gold or pearls or costly attire but by good deeds, as befits women who profess religion" (I Tim. 2:9-10). But in Revelation John shows an appreciation for the beauty of this gem in describing the New Jerusalem: "And the twelve gates were twelve pearls, each of the gates made of a single pearl, and the street of the city was pure gold, transparent as glass" (Rev. 21:21). This passage gave rise to the familiar phrase "pearly gates."

Mother-of-pearl, an important commercial product used for buttons and other accessories, is actually of the same substance as pearls, since it is the material that lines the inside of the oyster's shell. It is thin and flat, however, and lacks the luster of its "offspring" the pearl, so it has never been considered especially valuable. But paving a courtyard with

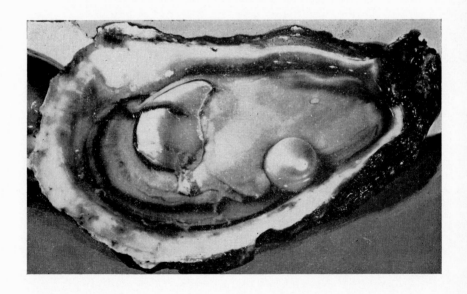

A "pearl of great value" is shown as it might appear to a fortunate pearl diver who has just opened up an oyster. The pearl is formed from the same substance that lines the oyster's shell. (Photograph courtesy of Ewing Galloway.)

259

it is another matter, especially when it is combined with other semiprecious materials—which is what was done at the palace of King Ahasuerus in the capital city of Susa: there was "a mosaic pavement of porphyry, marble, mother-of-pearl and precious stones" (Esther 1:6).

PRICE OF WISDOM

Throughout the Bible the pearl often symbolizes a standard of value, something to which other values are compared. According to the book of Job "the price of wisdom is above pearls" (Job 28:18). In the language of Jesus the pearl symbolizes spiritual treasure, and he warns: "Do not throw your pearls before swine" (Matt. 7:6). In one parable he compares the kingdom of heaven to a single pearl that is worth more than any other: "The kingdom of heaven is like a merchant in search of fine pearls, who, on finding one pearl of great value, went and sold all that he had and bought it" (Matt. 13:45-46). The person who finds the kingdom of heaven, who believes that God rules over all the world, has a treasure beyond all other treasures.

The Serpent

From the religion of ancient Egypt to the snake cults of our own day, the serpent has played an important part in the religions of mankind, and the Judeo-Christian tradition is no exception. But whereas in many religions this reptile is an object of veneration and even adoration, in Christianity it represents evil, and more specifically, the devil. The serpent is first mentioned in the familiar story of the Fall. It is the serpent, "more subtle than any other wild creature that the Lord God had made" (Gen. 3:1), who tempts Eve to taste the forbidden fruit, and it was inevitable that this creature later became identified with the Prince of Darkness.

The first specific mention of this association is found in the apocryphal Wisdom of Solomon, written around the time of the birth of Christ: "God created man for incorruption, and

---

CLASSIFICATION. *Echis colorata* (carpet viper); *Vipera palaestinae* (common Palestine viper); some species of genus *Cerastes;* all members of Viperidae family; *Naja haje* (Egyptian cobra), member of Elapidae family; both families of order Serpentes of Reptilia class of the vertebrates.

LEXICON. *Hebrew:* NACHASH (serpent); SARAPH (fiery serpent); TANNIN (serpent or dragon); EPHEH and TSIPHONI (vipers); SHEPHIPHON and AKSHUB (adders); PETHEN (asp). *Greek:* HERPETON (reptile); OPHIS (serpent); ECHIDNA (viper); ASPIS (asp).

made him in the image of his own eternity, but through the devil's envy death entered the world" (Wisd. of Sol. 2:23-24). In the last book of the Bible the identification has become definite: "The great dragon was thrown down, that ancient serpent, who is called the Devil and Satan, the deceiver of the whole world" (Rev. 12:9; cf. Rev. 20:2). Thus the sinister career of the serpent in the Bible extends from an insidious entry of evil into the goodness of the earth created by God, to the downfall of the serpent-devil when the Prince of Peace returns to complete the redemption of that same earth.

VARIETY OF ROLES

In between, the serpent has a variety of roles, most of them not nearly as symbolic as those cited above, but hardly any of them especially beneficial to mankind. The serpent represents danger in the language of many biblical writers, which is not surprising when one considers that of the thirty-six species of snake found in Palestine, a large number are poisonous. The biblical authors, close observers of nature, distinguished among the various species; seven, possibly eight, Hebrew words denote different kinds of serpents, and four Greek words are used in the New Testament. There are general words for "serpent" in both languages, but most of the rest are almost certainly intended to denote various kinds of poisonous snakes.

VIPERS OR COBRAS

Serpents comprise an entire order (Serpentes) of the reptile class of vertebrates. It is safe to assert that all of the poisonous snakes mentioned in the Bible are members of either the viper or the cobra families, but more positive identification is difficult and largely conjectural. Certain characteristics are shared by both of these families: their poison is a clear, thin secretion that is transmitted to the victim's blood stream by means of fangs. This venom may affect the respiratory organs and may also disintegrate blood cells or coagulate the blood. The cobra's venom, which resembles curare, causes death by suffocation within half an hour if injected into a major artery. Among the vipers that were probably known to biblical authors are the common Palestinian viper, the carpet viper, and vipers of the genus *Cerastes*. The representative of the cobras is the Egyptian cobra, commonly called the asp, which is often depicted in Egyptian art and even decorated the headgear of Egyptian royalty.

SNAKE'S VENOM

The author of the apocryphal Ecclesiastus declares: "There is no venom worse than a snake's venom" (Ecclus. 25:15), and this typifies the awed respect many biblical authors hold for poisonous snakes. Some seem to have thought that the serpent used its tongue to inject its venom, as in the statement: "The tongue of a viper will kill him" (Job 20:16). Similarly, a psalmist describes crafty people in this manner: "They make their tongue sharp as a serpent's, and under their lips is the poison of vipers" (Ps. 140:3). This statement seems to reflect a folk belief that the serpent "sharpens" its tongue, usually by honing it on a rock. One really cannot blame these writers for not observing the snake closely enough to determine the exact manner in which it strikes.

Even though biblical writers believed that a curse had been placed on the serpent by the Lord God at the time of the Fall (Gen. 3:14-15), it did not prevent them from also believing that even this creature could be used by the Lord to effect his retribution. Amos, speaking for God, asserts: "Though they [the obstinate and godless] hide themselves on the top of Carmel, from there I will search out and take them; and though they hide from my sight at the bottom of the sea, there I will command the serpent, and it shall bite them" (Amos 9:3). Later, the same prophet, in a magnificent piece of irony, describes the plight of mankind on the Day of the

The toothy serpent carved on this capital in the abbey church
of St. Benoit-sur-Loire is actually offering the fruit to Eve (left),
whose arm is missing. Adam cowers on the right in this eleventh-
century sculpture. (Photo by Gudiol.)

264

Lord: "It is . . . as if a man fled from a lion, and a bear met him; or went into the house and leaned with his hand against the wall, and a serpent bit him" (Amos 5:18-19). The best known biblical instance of the serpent carrying out the wrath of the Lord occurs in the Pentateuch, when the Israelites are punished for their incessant mutterings: "Then the Lord sent fiery serpents among the people, and they bit the people, so that many people of Israel died" (Num. 21:6). "Fiery" may refer to the effect of the bite, in which case it is possible the snakes were carpet vipers.

PAUL PROTECTED

There are other passages in the Bible in which men who believe in God are protected against the bite of the serpent. One of the signs that will be manifested when the disciples of Jesus "go into all the world and preach the gospel" is that "they will pick up serpents" (Mark 16:15, 18). This prediction of Jesus has been taken literally by certain small sects, part of whose ritual is the handling of poisonous snakes. Earlier Jesus had welcomed the seventy disciples back from their first mission with these words: "Behold, I have given you authority to tread upon serpents and scorpions" (Luke 10:19). For the Apostle Paul these promises came to pass when he was shipwrecked on Malta during his last voyage to Rome. Paul picked up a bundle of sticks to throw on the fire around which he and his companions were warming themselves and a viper crept out and attached itself to his hand. The Maltese who were watching decided that the wrath of the gods had caught up with this man who had so miraculously escaped drowning, but when Paul calmly shook the snake off his hand and into the fire and went about his business, "they changed their minds and said that he was a god" (Acts 28:1-6).

There are a number of interesting observations about the habits of serpents in the Bible. For instance, a proverbist rhapsodizes: "Three things are too wonderful for me; four I do not understand: the way of an eagle in the sky, the way of a serpent on a rock, the way of a ship on the high seas, and the way of a man with a maiden" (Prov. 30:18-19). Apparently he is thinking of the slithering movement of the snake across a barren rock, and the contrast of its colors with the gray background. In the book of Ecclesiastes we find the statement: "A serpent will bite him who breaks through a wall" (Eccles. 10:8). A snake often takes refuge in the crevices between sections of a stone wall.

"WISE AS SERPENTS"

Few Old Testament authors, except in Genesis 3, are impressed by the craftiness or wisdom of the serpent, but Jesus obviously remembered that it was "more subtle than any other wild creature" when he instructed his disciples: "Behold, I send you out as sheep in the midst of wolves; so be wise as serpents and innocent as doves" (Matt. 10:16). He wants his followers to be pure in heart, but also to use their mental resources—to be crafty and cautious when the situation requires it.

SNAKES MAGICAL

Serpents have been associated throughout the ages with magic and necromancy. An example is found in the story of Moses and Aaron: "Aaron cast down his rod before Pharaoh and his servants, and it became a serpent. Then Pharaoh summoned the wise men and the sorcerers; and they also, the magicians of Egypt, did the same by their secret arts. For every man cast down his rod, and they became serpents. But Aaron's rod swallowed up their rods" (Exod. 7:10-12). There are snake charmers in Egypt even today, and perhaps the Egyptian magicians were able to induce their snakes to be as rigid as rods. The fact that Aaron's rod consumed those of the Egyptians is presented as evidence that the power of God is greater than any tricks performed by Pharaoh's men. The

snake that is "charmed" in Egypt today, in the familiar manner of playing the flute and making it sway to the music (even
though snakes are deaf), is the Egyptian cobra or asp, a dangerous rust-colored serpent that reaches a length of some
seven feet. A snake charmer is mentioned by a psalmist in
his complaint about unjust judges: "They have venom like
the venom of a serpent, like the deaf adder that stops its ear,
so that it does not hear the voice of charmers or of the cunning
enchanter" (Ps. 58:4-5).

Always the biblical writers come back to the chief association of the serpent, sinfulness. In Ecclesiasticus we are warned:
"Flee from sin as from a snake; for if you approach sin, it
will bite you" (Ecclus. 21:2). With fine scorn, John the Baptist
called out to the Sadducees and Pharisees who had come out
to hear him: "You brood of vipers! Who warned you to flee
from the wrath to come?" (Matt. 3:7).

Coiled and at rest, but still alert, this bronze serpent is difficult
to identify as any particular species. Since it was created by
an ancient Egyptian artist, it may depict the Egyptian cobra.
(Photograph courtesy of the Oriental Institute of the University
of Chicago.)

The Snail

The little mollusk called the snail is mentioned only once in the Bible, and there is even some doubt about that reference, but a product made from the snail figures in biblical accounts of royalty and the priesthood. That product is a purple dye, produced by a gland of the *Murex trunculus,* the *Murex brandaris,* and the *Purpura haemastoma,* and it formed the basis for an important drygoods industry in biblical times. Like material dyed with scarlet (see "The Kermes"), purple yarns and cloth were expensive and available only to the relatively well-to-do.

The three snails with "purple glands" were found along the coasts of the Mediterranean, and coast dwellers such as the Phoenicians and Romans were particularly interested in collecting and processing them. An ancient myth says that during the reign of Phoenix, the first king of Tyre, the unique facility of these snails was discovered when a shepherd's dog chewed on one and his nose turned purple. However true this is, the Phoenicians, the Egyptians, and the Assyrians all began to use purple dye from the snail around 1500 B.C.

CLASSIFICATION. *Murex brandaris, Murex trunculus, Purpura haemastoma,* all members of Helicidae family of order Pulmonata of Gastropoda class (snails and slugs) of phylum Mollusca.

LEXICON. *Hebrew:* SHABLUL (snail); ARGAMAN, ARGEVAN (purple). *Greek:* PORPHURA, PORPHUREOS (purple).

Purple fishermen, who were a significant enough part of the economy to form their own guild during the time of the Roman Empire, harvested snails during the fall and winter seasons, either with baited traps and nets or by diving for them in the manner of pearl divers (see "The Pearl Oyster"). In spring the egg-laying takes place and the juices of the snail are poor, and in summer the snails remain concealed. The processing consisted of crushing the smaller snails and removing the part of larger snails that contained the gland, placing these in a salt solution for three days, and then heating the liquid in lead kettles for ten days. The mixture was then reduced by boiling to about one-sixteenth of its original volume, and the unwanted snail remnants were strained off. This concentrated product was sold on the market, but before it was used in dyeing it had to be diluted with water, and other substances such as honey added to ensure that the dye would "fix." Wool was dipped in this solution and then hung up to dry in the sun. After it was dry it was ready to go to the market, and a female seller of such material is mentioned in the book of Acts: "A woman named Lydia, from the city of Thyatira, a seller of purple goods, who was a worshiper of God" (Acts 16:14).

PURPLE "STUFF"

Purple was used much earlier than the first century A.D. by the Israelites, the earliest recorded instance being the preparation of Aaron's priestly garments during the Israelites' sojourn in the desert. In those times only raw wool and spun yarn were dyed, never finished cloth, and the references in the book of Exodus are all to purple yarn or "stuff." The narrative informs us that "of the blue and purple and scarlet stuff they made finely wrought garments, for ministering in the holy place" (Exod. 39:1). In addition, the Israelites "made the ephod of gold, blue and purple and scarlet stuff, and fine twined linen" (Exod. 39:2), and "gold leaf was ham-

From tiny marine snails similar to this one, people of the Near East manufactured a costly purple dye. Legend says that this use of the snail was discovered when a dog ate a snail it found on a beach, and its nose turned purple. (Wide World Photos.)

mered out and cut into threads to work into the blue and purple and the scarlet stuff" (Exod. 39:3).

THE PRICE OF PURPLE

But the price of purple was high—in the time of Marcus Aurelius it cost almost a thousand dollars for one pound of purple wool—and few besides kings could afford it in any quantity. King Ahasuerus in the book of Esther had his palace decorated for a feast with "white cotton curtains and blue hangings caught up with cords of fine linen and purple to silver rings (Esther 1:6). Later in the story of Esther, Mordecai is rewarded by the king in this fashion: he "went out from the presence of the king in royal robes of blue and white, with a great golden crown and a mantle of fine linen and purple" (Esther 8:15). King Solomon of course would have purple yarn at his disposal, and he requested King Huram of Tyre to send him "a man skilled to work . . . in purple, crimson, and blue fabrics" (II Chron. 2:7) to aid in the adornment of the temple in Jerusalem.

The few people who were not kings and yet could afford purple were very rich indeed. This fact should help us understand more fully Jesus' parable of the rich man and Lazarus: "There was a rich man, who was clothed in purple and fine linen" (Luke 16:19). This, in contrast to the complete poverty of Lazarus, shows the transitory nature of human wealth when the roles of the two men are reversed in the afterlife. The harlot of Babylon described in the book of Revelation symbolizes, at least in part, human wealth and greed, and so is "arrayed in purple and scarlet, and bedecked with gold and jewels and pearls" (Rev. 17:4).

ALL FROM HUMBLE SNAIL

But one must remember that this splendor is derived from the humble and insignificant snail. Except for its use in making dye, which has largely passed from commercial importance in our day, the only other use by humans of any member of this very large zoological order is as a gourmet food, a practice unknown in biblical times. The single specific mention of the snail is in the Psalms; the poet declares: "Let them [the impious] be like the snail which dissolves into slime" (Ps. 58:8). The "slime" is a reference to the substance secreted by the snail over which it moves; legless, it eases its laborious passage from place to place by this means. This passage in the Psalms reflects an ancient superstition that the snail is dissolved slowly by its own slime and eventually perishes in it.

Appendix
Miscellany of Creatures

Appendix
Miscellany of Creatures

Included here are all forms of animal life that are not included in the main text of this book, but are mentioned in either the RSV or KJV texts of the Bible, as well as some which are not mentioned in either, but for which there is reason to believe that they are intended by the Hebrew or Greek texts.

MAMMALS

BABOON

Not appearing in either the RSV or KJV, the baboon was undoubtedly known to the Israelites at some stage of their history. The "apes" that were sent to King Solomon's court may possibly have been baboons (see "The Ape"), but it is more likely that the "peacocks" that accompanied them were actually baboons (I Kings 10:22; II Chron. 9:21).

> CLASSIFICATION. Some species of genus *Papio*, members of Cercopithecidae family of order Primates.
> LEXICON. *Hebrew:* TUKKIYYIM.

BADGER (RSV only)

There is no evidence that any member of the badger family was ever to be found in the vicinity of Palestine. It is used in the RSV to denote the hyrax (q.v.) and to translate *tachash* (see "The Sea Cow").

> CLASSIFICATION. *Meles meles* (common European badger), member of Mustelidae family of order Carnivora.
> LEXICON. *Hebrew:* TACHASH.

CHAMOIS (KJV only)

This is an acceptable translation of *zemer* (Deut. 14:5), one of several Hebrew words for antelope (see "The Antelopes"). Known for the uses made of its hide, the chamois is native to Asia Minor and is a remarkable climber and leaper, with unusually sharp eyesight and hearing.

> CLASSIFICATION. *Rupicapra rupicapra,* member of Bovidae family of order Artiodactyla (even-toed hoofed mammals).
> LEXICON. *Hebrew:* ZEMER.

ELEPHANT

Although it never makes an appearance in the Bible itself, the elephant is nevertheless represented there by its tusks. There are a number of references to ivory, which was apparently imported to Palestine (I Kings 10:22; II Chron. 9:21), although before 1500 B.C. elephants were to be found in western Asia. The Israelites considered ivory to be beautiful and luxurious (II Chron. 9:17; Ps. 45:8; Song of Sol. 5:14; 7:4; Ezek. 27:6); and one prophet also associated it with evil (Amos 3:15; 6:4). Both the African and Indian species may have been the source of the ivory mentioned in the Bible. In Hellenistic times elephants were used in warfare, and the apocryphal I Maccabees makes mention of "thirty-two elephants accustomed to war" (I Mac. 6:30).

> CLASSIFICATION. *Elephas indicus* (Indian elephant) and *Loxodonta africana* (African elephant), members of Elephantidae family of order Proboscidea.
> LEXICON. *Hebrew:* SHEN, SHENHABBIM. *Greek:* ELEPHANTINOS.

FALLOW DEER (KVJ only)

It is difficult to make specific identifications of the kinds of deer mentioned in the Bible (see "The Deer"), but this particular species was found in Palestine in biblical times. Smaller than the common red deer, it is only three feet high at the shoulder, and is a yellowish-brown color.

CLASSIFICATION. *Dama mesopotamica* (Persian fallow deer), member of Cervidae family of order Artiodactyla.

LEXICON. *Hebrew:* YACHMUR.

HEDGEHOG (RSV only)
There is considerable doubt among biblical scholars whether the Hebrew word *qippod* should be translated "bittern" (q.v.), as it is in the King James, German, and Scandinavian Bibles. The hedgehog is suggested as a substitute, and it suits the context except in one passage where it is found on top of a pillar (Zeph. 2:14). A hedgehog would be unable to climb a pillar, but since the building in question is in ruins, it is possible that the pillar is lying on its side. The hedgehog is a small insect-eating mammal with short spines that rolls itself into a ball for protection and hibernates in a nest of leaves; it is often found in ruins and deserted habitations.

CLASSIFICATION. *Erinaceus europaeus* (common hedgehog), member of Erinaceidae family of order Insectivora.

LEXICON. *Hebrew:* QIPPOD.

HYENA (RSV only)
There is little doubt that the hyena was found in ancient Palestine, but there is somewhat more doubt that it is mentioned by name in the Bible, except in the place name Zeboim (I Sam. 13:18; Neh. 11:34) or Zeboiim (Gen. 10:19; 14:2; 14:8; Hos. 11:8). The word generally translated as "jackal" (q.v.) may often refer to hyenas, since the two animals have such similar habits; they both are carrion-eaters, and both are noted for their mournful howls (Isa. 13:22). Hyenas, however, form a separate family of carnivores.

CLASSIFICATION. *Hyaena hyaena* (common hyena) or *Hyaena striata* (striped hyena), members of Hyaenidae family of order Carnivora.

LEXICON. *Hebrew:* IYYIM(?).

Mole

Neither moles nor their close relatives the shrews are found in Palestine, and it is almost certain that the Hebrew word *chapharperah* denotes the mole rat (q.v.). The KJV includes the mole in one list of unclean animals (Lev. 11:30), but there is no basis for this and the animal in question is probably a chameleon (see "The Lizard").

> CLASSIFICATION. Some species of genus *Talpa* of Talpidae family of order Insectivora.
> LEXICON. *Hebrew:* CHAPHARPERAH.

Mountain-sheep (RSV only)

This is the RSV rendering of *zemer* (Deut. 14:5), replacing the "chamois" (see above) of the KJV. Since some sort of antelope (q.v.) is probably intended here, it is not very likely that the Bible is referring to a wild sheep, although several varieties of sheep (q.v.) are native to the Near East, including the Cyprian red sheep and the Barbary sheep.

> CLASSIFICATION. *Ovis orientalis* (Cyprian red sheep) and *Ammotragus lervia* (Barbary sheep), members of Bovidae family of order Artiodactyla.
> LEXICON. *Hebrew:* ZEMER.

Porcupine (RSV only)

The RSV renders *qippod* as "hedgehog" (see above) in two places, but chooses porcupine for the third (Isa. 34:11). In every case "bittern" (q.v.) is the choice of the KJV. The porcupine is vaguely similar to the hedgehog in appearance, but belongs to a different order, is larger than the hedgehog, and has quills rather than spines covering its body. It is, however, found in Palestine today, and may be the animal meant in the Bible.

> CLASSIFICATION. *Hystrix cristata* (common or crested porcupine), member of Hystricidae family of order Rodentia.
> LEXICON. *Hebrew:* QIPPOD.

Roe, Roebuck (RSV only)

Instead of identifying *yachmur* as the fallow deer (see above), the RSV chooses the roe deer, which is a very beautiful and graceful animal, but which was probably unknown to biblical writers.

> Classification. *Capreolus capreolus*, member of Cervidae family of order Artiodactyla.
> Lexicon. *Hebrew:* YACHMUR.

Whale

The whale is mentioned specifically only once in the Bible, and only in the RSV, in a New Testament reference to the story of Jonah (Matt. 12:40). However, the creature in the book of Jonah (1:17) is described only as a great fish (q.v.), probably meaning a shark. There are several whales native to the Mediterranean, including the humpback whale and the fin whale, and their near relatives the dolphins, all of which may have been known to biblical writers. Several references to "sea monsters" and "dragons" (*tannin* in the Hebrew) are possibly to be understood as whales.

> Classification. *Megaptera böops* (humpback whale) and some species of genus *Balaenoptera* (fin whales), members of Balaenopteridae family; Delphinidae family (dolphins); both families of order Cetacea.
> Lexicon. *Greek:* KETOS (whale).

Wild Ass or Onager

Many of the references to the ass (q.v.) in the Bible probably denote the onager, which is the variety that may be seen in most zoos. It roams Persia, and was formerly more widespread.

> Classification. *Equus hemionus hemihippus*, member of Equidae family of order Perissodactyla.
> Lexicon. *Hebrew:* PERE, ARAD.

279

WILD GOAT or IBEX (RSV only)

The Nubian ibex may be found today in large numbers in the district of the Dead Sea. There is thus little doubt that several of the many biblical references to the goat (q.v.) denote this animal or some near relative.

CLASSIFICATION. *Capra ibex nubiana,* member of Bovidae family of order Artiodactyla.
LEXICON. *Hebrew:* YEELIM.

WILD OX

The animal from which domestic cattle were bred may well have been known to biblical writers. The KJV refers to it only once (Deut. 14:5), in translating *teo,* which is more likely an antelope (q.v.). Where the KJV uses "unicorn," the RSV has "wild ox," as in the Lord's answer to Job out of the whirlwind: "Is the wild ox willing to serve you?" (Job 39:9).

CLASSIFICATION. *Bos primigenius,* member of Bovidae family of order Artiodactyla.
LEXICON. *Hebrew:* REEM.

BIRDS

CUCKOO (KJV only)

Included in the list of unclean birds in the KJV (Lev. 11:16; Deut. 14:15), the cuckoo is represented in Palestine during the summer by two species. It is unlikely that the Hebrew word *shachaph* refers to this bird, however; it is probably some kind of owl (q.v.).

CLASSIFICATION. *Cuculus canorus canorus* (common cuckoo) and *Clamator glandarius* (great spotted cuckoo), members of the Cuculidae family of order Cuculiformes.
LEXICON. *Hebrew:* SHACHAPH.

Hoopoe (RSV only)

A likely candidate for the list of unclean birds in the Mosaic law is the hoopoe (Lev. 11:19; Deut. 14:18), which is often seen searching for grubs in dunghills with its long, thin bill. Related to the kingfishers, it is represented in the Near East by several species.

> CLASSIFICATION. Some species of genus *Upapa*, member of Upupidae family of order Coraciiformes.
> LEXICON. *Hebrew:* DUKIPHATH.

Ibis (RSV only)

The Israelites were undoubtedly familiar with the Egyptian red ibis and perhaps some other species, but there is no evidence to support the reading in Lev. 11:17 of the RSV. The bird in question is probably an owl (q.v.), an interpretation used by the RSV itself in Deut. 14:16.

> CLASSIFICATION. *Threskiornis aethiopica aethiopica,* member of Threskiornithidae family of order Ciconiiformes.
> LEXICON. *Hebrew:* YANSHUPH.

Lapwing (KJV only)

This is the KJV translation of *dukiphath,* which appears as "hoopoe" (see above) in the RSV. The lapwing is found in Palestine in the summer, but all evidence points to "hoopoe" as the correct translation.

> CLASSIFICATION. *Vanellus vanellus,* member of Vanellinae subfamily of order Charadriiformes.
> LEXICON. *Hebrew:* DUKIPHATH.

Nighthawk

The common nighthawk, found only in North America, is a relative of the nightjar, which may be the bird referred to as "nighthawk" in the dietary laws (Lev. 11:16; Deut. 14:15) by both the RSV and the KJV. Three species have been seen in Palestine, but the Hebrew word *tachmas* is probably to be understood as a kind of owl (q.v.).

> CLASSIFICATION. Some species of genus *Caprimulgus* (nightjars), members of Caprimulgidae family of order Caprimulgiformes.
> LEXICON. *Hebrew:* TACHMAS.

SEA GULL (RSV only)

A number of sea gulls, as well as petrels and shearwaters, are native to the coastal area of Palestine. Once again, given the context in which the bird appears (the unclean animals; Lev. 11:16; Deut. 14:15), a kind of owl (q.v.) is probably meant, although there is some support for this translation.

> CLASSIFICATION. *Larus canus* (common gull), member of Laridae family; Procellariidae family (petrels and shearwaters); both families of order Charadriiformes.
> LEXICON. *Hebrew:* SHACHAPH.

SPECKLED BIRD OF PREY

No one has been able to positively identify the creature in Jer. 12:9, which is *tsabua ayit* in Hebrew. There is speculation that a hyena or a jackal (q.v.) is meant here.

SWAN (KJV only)

There is little to substantiate this translation (in Lev. 11:18 and Deut. 14:16) of the Hebrew *tinshemeth*, for the swan is rarely seen in Palestine. See "The Owl," and the Water Hen below.

> CLASSIFICATION. Some species of genus *Cygnus*, members of Anatidae family of order Anseriformes.
> LEXICON. *Hebrew:* TINSHEMETH.

WATER HEN (RSV only)

This is one of the RSV renderings of *tinshemeth*, and is only slightly more defensible than "swan." The water hen, a member of the rail family, is not seen in Palestine, but a close relative, the purple gallinule, is. See "The Owl."

> CLASSIFICATION. *Porphyrio porphyrio* (purple gallinule), member of Rallidae family of order Gruiformes.
> LEXICON. *Hebrew:* TINSHEMETH.

INSECTS

BEETLE (KJV only)
True beetles form the largest single order of insects, but there is little evidence to support this reading of the Hebrew *chargol* in the dietary laws (Lev. 11:22). The insect in question is more likely a kind of locust (q.v.).

> CLASSIFICATION. Some species of order Coleoptera.
> LEXICON. *Hebrew:* CHARGOL.

CRICKET (RSV only)
The RSV renders *chargol* as "cricket," denoting a family that belongs to the same order as the locusts (q.v.). As in the case of the King James's "beetle," "locust" is probably the best translation.

> CLASSIFICATION. Gryllidae family of order Orthoptera.
> LEXICON. *Hebrew:* CHARGOL.

LICE (KJV only)
This is a reasonable alternative to the gnats of the third plague in Egypt (Exod. 8:16-19), since lice were particularly abhorrent to the Egyptians. These wingless insects are parasites and are classified according to the type of animal they prey upon.

> CLASSIFICATION. *Pediculus humanus* (human body louse), member of Pediculidae family of order Anoplura.
> LEXICON. *Hebrew:* KEN, KINNAM.

283

MANNA

It is fairly well established that the "manna" that sustained the Israelites in the wilderness was a sweet secretion of two scale insects that live on twigs of the tamarisk bush. It was a "fine, flake-like thing, fine as hoarfrost. . . . It was like coriander seed, white, and the taste of it was like wafers made with honey" (Exod. 16:14, 31). This rare event can still be observed in the desert today, wherever tamarisk scales are found; in fact, certain plant lice, or aphids, produce a similar secretion. The rapid evaporation that takes place in the dry air of the desert causes the insects' secretion to solidify, and this secretion has a very high sugar content.

> CLASSIFICATION. *Trabutina mannipara* and *Najacococcus serpentinus minor* (tamarisk scales), members of family Coccidea of order Hemiptera.
>
> LEXICON. *Hebrew:* MAN. *Greek:* MANNA.

MISCELLANEOUS

CORAL

Among the adornments to be found in palaces and fine houses in biblical times was undoubtedly the red coral, but there is some dispute as to whether it is actually mentioned in the Hebrew. One of the words so translated, the Hebrew *peninim* in Lam. 4:7, is usually rendered elsewhere as "pearls," or as "jewels" or "costly stones." There is a greater possibility that *ramoth* in Job 28:18 and Ezek. 27:16 refers to the red coral.

> CLASSIFICATION. *Corallium nobile,* member of Gorgoniidae family of order Gorgonacea of Anthozoa class of phylum Coelenterata (polyps, jellyfish, sea anemone).
>
> LEXICON. *Hebrew:* RAMOTH, PENINIM.

SPONGE

The sponge is, of course, the skeleton of a marine animal (as is the decorative coral). It appears in the Bible during the crucifixion, when Jesus is offered a sponge soaked in sour wine while he is hanging on the cross (Matt. 27:48; Mark 15:36; John 19:29).

> CLASSIFICATION. Some species of genus *Spongia* (including many of the commercial sponges), members of Spongiidae family of order Ceratosa of Demospongia class of phylum Porifera.
> LEXICON. *Greek:* SPOGGOS.

TORTOISE (KJV only)

There is little substantiation for this rendering in Lev. 11:29 of the Hebrew word *tsab,* which is undoubtedly to be understood as a kind of lizard (q.v.). The "land tortoise" would be any member of the genus *Testudo.*

> CLASSIFICATION. Some species of genus *Testudo,* members of order Testudinata of Reptilia class of the vertebrates.
> LEXICON. *Hebrew:* TSAB.

TURTLE (KJV only)

This animal is not to be understood as a reptile, but is an Elizabethan form of "turtledove" (see "The Dove").

WORM

There is probably no actual reference in the Bible to earthworms, and wherever "worm" appears it should be understood as "maggot" or "caterpillar." See "The Fly" and "The Moth."

Note: FABULOUS CREATURES

The KJV makes reference to several fabulous creatures—such as the cockatrice, sea dragon, and unicorn. In some cases mythical creatures are obviously intended in the Hebrew or Greek texts themselves; in others, the KJV translators were simply availing themselves of the natural history current in the seventeenth century. Into this latter category would fall several references to the cockatrice (Isa. 11:8; 14:29; 59:5; Jer. 8:17), a kind of serpent hatched from a chicken egg by a serpent, a few of the references to dragons and sea monsters (see "The Jackal," and the Whale above), and the unicorn (see the Wild Ox above).

Indexes

Index of Creatures

References to main entries are in **boldface** type.

Index of
Biblical Names and Places

294

Scriptural Index

25:32, 34, 41—44
26:34—128
27:28—217
27:48—285

Mark
1:6—29, 222
5:11-13—116
7:27—37
7:28—37
13:35—128
15:36—285
16:15, 18—265

Luke
2:8—104
5:4—243
5:5—243
5:9—243
9:10-17—244
10:19—229, 265
11:11-12—229
12:6—180
12:24—177
12:33—225
13:15—14, 87
13:31-32—39
13:34—127
14:19—90
15:20—113
15:23—87
15:29—45
16:19—271
17:2—15
24:42-43—244

John
1:32—137
1:36—137
10:4—102
10:11—103
10:12—122
12:14-15—13
19:29—285
21:13—244

Acts
8:32—101
16:14—269
20:29—122
26:14—91
28:1-6—265

I Corinthians
9:7—103

Philippians
3:2—37

I Timothy
2:9-10—259

Hebrews
11:37—48

James
3:3—62
5:2—225

I Peter
5:8—77

II Peter
2:22—37, 113

Revelation
1:14—106
6:1-8—62
9:3—220
9:3, 5—229
12:9—262
12:14—141
16:13—248
17:1-6—217
17:4—258, 271
18:11-12—217
18:16—217
20:2—262
21:21—259
22:15—37

APOCRYPHA

Judith
10:21—211

Wisdom of Solomon
2:23-24—262

Ecclesiasticus
21:2—267
25:15—263
26:7—228
39:30-31—228

Maccabees I
whole book—114
6:30—276

Body, 11 on 14 Caledonia
Display, Tempo
Paper, Carfax E. F.